Virology

A SCOPE® PUBLICATION

Dale A. Stringfellow, PhD
Guest Editor-in-Chief

James F. Bale, Jr, MD
Lawrence Corey, MD
Robert B. Couch, MD
Lowell A. Glasgow, MD†
Earl R. Kern, PhD
David A. Lennette, PhD
Evelyne T. Lennette, PhD
Fred Rapp, PhD
Lawrence R. Stanberry, MD, PhD

†Doctor Glasgow died February 4, 1982.

ISBN 0-89501-013-5

8801-36R2

Contents

Preface

Viruses are unique, obligate intracellular parasites. Because they are so small and depend on host cells for survival and propagation, less is known about viruses than about other microorganisms and how they replicate, how they interact with normal cell function, or how they cause acute, chronic, or latent diseases.

More than 60% of the patients a physician sees each year for infectious diseases suffer from viral infections. This proportion will undoubtedly increase as new viruses are linked to diseases now poorly understood and as more effective means of diagnosing, preventing, and treating viral diseases are developed. Antiviral chemotherapy and rapid diagnosis of viral infections will become extremely important to the practicing physician over the next few years.

This monograph was written by outstanding investigators, many of whom have spent their entire research and teaching careers studying viruses. The authors have provided unique insights into the topics they addressed. This monograph is dedicated to new investigators who will continue the quest begun decades ago to understand viruses and to control the diseases they cause.

Dale A. Stringfellow, PhD

Nature and Classification of Viruses

Fred Rapp, PhD

Evan Pugh Professor of Microbiology
American Cancer Society Professor of Virology
Professor and Chairman,
Department of Microbiology
The Milton S. Hershey Medical Center
The Pennsylvania State University
Hershey, PA 17033

GENERAL PROPERTIES OF VIRUSES

Viruses are unique infectious microorganisms that have several distinguishing properties. Originally, their small size distinguished them from other infectious agents: they pass through filters that retain bacteria. Figure 1.1 shows relative sizes of a variety of viruses that produce infection in humans. It also shows two bacteria *(Escherichia coli,* which is a fairly typically sized bacterium, and *Chlamydia,* which is an unusually small bacterium) and a number of bacterial and plant viruses.

Viruses are distinguishable also by their obligate intracellular parasitism, simple organization, mode of replication, and nucleic acid content. Viruses grow in other cells because virus particles lack energy-synthesizing organelles, enzyme systems, and protein-synthesizing machinery. Viruses reproduce by assembling subunits into infectious particles, not by dividing, as other microorganisms do. The infectious particle of a virus is the virion, which is essentially a mass of DNA or RNA capable of autonomous replication and surrounded by a protein coat. The viral genome (hereditary material) is either DNA or RNA, *but never both.* Distinctive features of viruses and other microorganisms are listed in the Table.

Based on their unique features, viruses may be defined as small intracellular parasites that contain either DNA or RNA, reproduce by synthesis of subunits within a host cell, and cause disease as a consequence of replication, the process of the assembly and release of infectious virus particles. The virus life cycle has two phases, the extracellular phase and the intracellular phase; the extracellular virus particle (virion) is the infectious agent that intracellularly causes disease by killing or altering the cell it invades.

VIRION STRUCTURE

Detection of viruses in clinical specimens is closely tied to structural components of the virus, and classification and identification of viruses in clinical specimens are based largely on virion morphology and substructure. A typical virion is schematically diagrammed in Figure 1.2.

A virion has at least two components: (1) one or more molecules of either DNA or RNA, referred to as the genome, and (2) an outer symmetrical protein shell known as the capsid. The capsid is composed of individual polypeptides called protomers, which are coded by the virus. During assembly of capsids, one or more types of protomers aggregate into clusters called capsomers, which are recognizable in the electron microscope. The number and the appearance of capsomers are characteristic of a virus and important in its identification. The nucleic acid and capsid together are called the nucleocapsid. The capsid performs four functions: (1) It protects the nucleic acid from damage in the external environment, (2) it facilitates attachment to susceptible cells, (3) it confers structural symmetry on the virion, and (4) it confers antigenicity.

SYMMETRY OF NUCLEOCAPSIDS

Members of some virus families are composed of only a nucleic acid core and capsid; viruses of this type are called *naked viruses.* In members of other virus families, the nucleocapsid is surrounded by an envelope. Like the capsid, the envelope contains many copies of a few polypeptide chains. The proteins of the envelope are determined by viral genes. Individual polypeptides in the envelope are called peplomers and are inserted into the existing cellular membrane during intracellular growth; they usually protrude like spikes from the membrane.

Often these proteins are glycosylated by cellular enzymes into glycoprotein spikes. In contrast to the viral-determined envelope proteins, lipid and carbohydrate portions of the envelope's glycoprotein spikes are determined by the host cell. The spikes on envelope proteins are responsible for attachment to host cells, represent new and distinct antigens, and may have an enzymatic function. As with capsid subunits, peplomers may be of

Figure 1.1. Comparisons of the sizes of various human viruses, *Chlamydia*, *Escherichia coli*, and selected bacterial and plant viruses.

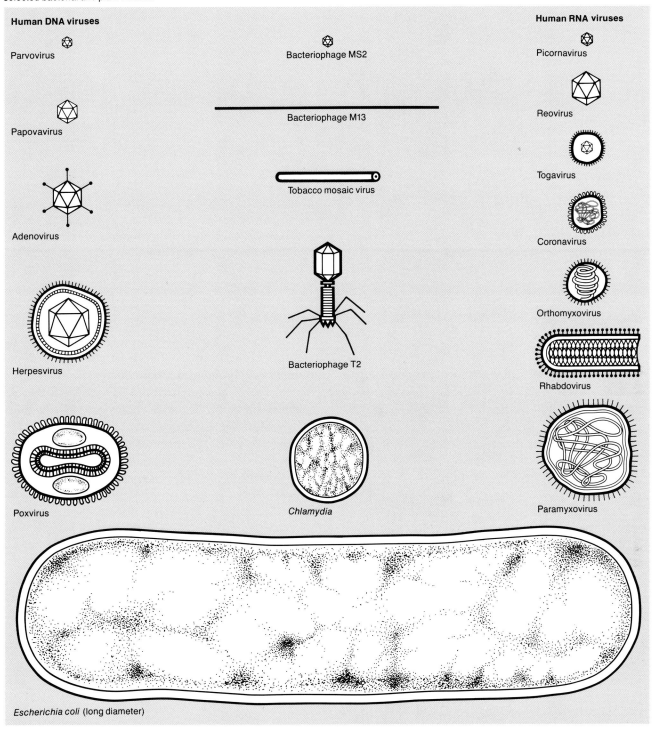

Human DNA viruses

Parvovirus

Papovavirus

Adenovirus

Herpesvirus

Poxvirus

Bacteriophage MS2

Bacteriophage M13

Tobacco mosaic virus

Bacteriophage T2

Chlamydia

Human RNA viruses

Picornavirus

Reovirus

Togavirus

Coronavirus

Orthomyxovirus

Rhabdovirus

Paramyxovirus

Escherichia coli (long diameter)

Table
Comparison of properties of infectious microorganisms

Characteristic	Microorganism				
	Mycoplasmas	Bacteria	*Chlamydia*	Rickettsiae	Viruses
Growth outside host cell	Yes	Yes	No	No	No
Independent protein synthesis	Yes	Yes	Yes	Yes	No
Generation of metabolic energy	Yes	Yes	No	Yes	No
Rigid envelope	No	Yes	Variable	Yes	Variable
Antibiotic susceptibility	Yes	Yes	Yes	Yes	No
Mode of reproduction	Fission	Fission	Fission	Fission	Host cell synthesis of subunits; then assembly of virion
Nucleic acids	DNA & RNA	DNA & RNA	DNA & RNA	DNA & RNA	DNA or RNA, not both

12

Figure 1.2. Components of the complete virus particle, or virion.

Figure 1.3. Structure of an envelope of an influenza virus particle.

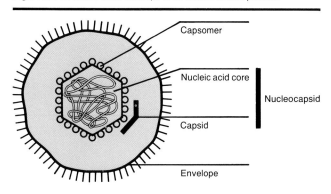

Capsomer

Nucleic acid core

Nucleocapsid

Capsid

Envelope

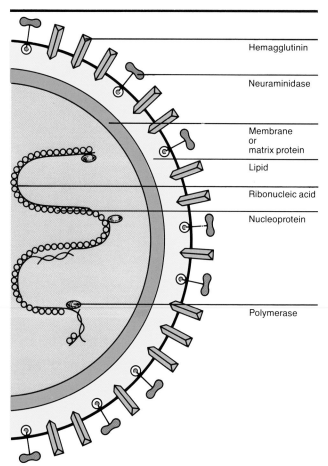

Hemagglutinin

Neuraminidase

Membrane or matrix protein

Lipid

Ribonucleic acid

Nucleoprotein

Polymerase

more than one type. Figure 1.3 shows a section of the envelope of influenza virus. Morphologically, hemagglutinin and neuraminidase spikes are identifiable, and each performs a different function. Among DNA-containing viruses, only the herpesviruses and the hepatitis B virus have envelopes; among RNA-containing viruses, all the helical viruses and the cubic togaviruses have envelopes. These viruses require that the envelope enter and infect the host cell.

Nucleocapsid symmetry may be icosahedral or helical. In icosahedral viruses, individual spheres represent capsomers, which are arranged into 20 equilateral triangular planes with 12 vertices, thus forming an icosahedron (Figure 1.4). Icosahedral viruses are also called cubic viruses or, sometimes, spherical viruses. Both of these synonyms represent descriptions of early electron microscopic findings, which revealed only the general shapes of virus particles. One important characteristic of an icosahedral capsid is its rigidity. The size of an icosahedral capsid is determined solely by the polypeptides (number of capsomers) that compose it. This size limits the amount of nucleic acid that can be encapsidated, but capsids that contain no nucleic acid have the same size and shape as capsids that are full. All DNA-containing animal viruses are icosahedral (poxviruses are complex), whereas RNA-containing viruses may be icosahedral or helical.

In helical, or coiled, viruses, the capsid is composed of identical protomers arranged in a helix with the nucleic acid coiled between the turns of the helix (Figure 1.5). The diameter of the helix is determined by the size and shape of the protomers, but its length depends upon the length of the RNA molecule enclosed. In contrast to the rigid icosahedral capsid, the helical capsid is extremely flexible. This flexibility permits considerable variability in configuration of the nucleocapsid and accounts for the variety of shapes (pleomorphism) of certain viruses, eg, parainfluenza virus.

A few viruses do not fit neatly into either the icosahedral or helical category. One such example is poxvirus, which is the largest animal virus and is larger than the small bacterium *Chlamydia*. Poxviruses have been arbitrarily classified as complex, or *binal*, viruses. Because of their complexity, there is disagreement concerning what constitutes their nucleocapsid. The nucleocapsid is surrounded by a lipid-containing layer; however, the lipid is not derived from host membrane and, therefore, is not a true envelope.

A second important human virus with multiple forms is the hepatitis B virus (Figure 1.6). The infectious particle, known as the Dane particle, consists of an envelope that can be overproduced to form small particles composed of hepatitis B surface antigen or long filaments. The hepatitis B nucleic acid, a double-stranded circular DNA with a break in one strand and a gap in the other, is the smallest known in human viruses.

The structure of reoviruses is unique. The virion is nonenveloped but has two shells: an icosahedral nucleocapsid surrounded by an icosahedral capsid. The double-stranded RNA genome has ten segments, and the total protein complement of the virion is ten or 11 proteins, so each RNA segment appears to code for one protein. Because most RNA-virus inclusion bodies stain red with acridine orange, the abnormal green-yellow staining of reovirus-infected cells originally led to the discovery that reovirus RNA is double stranded.

Replication does not require the cell nucleus and is confined to the cytoplasm. The viruses produce cytoplasmic inclusion bodies, which are the sites of core and capsid assembly.

Figure 1.4. Model of adenovirus with 252 spheres in icosahedral symmetry.

Figure 1.5. Model of measles virion, a helical virus.

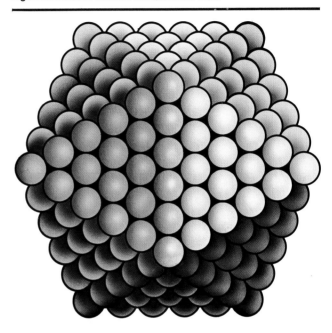

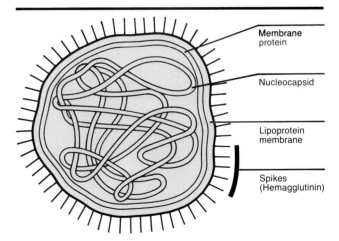

Membrane protein

Nucleocapsid

Lipoprotein membrane

Spikes (Hemagglutinin)

Figure 1.6. Structures of hepatitis B virus and antibody.

Dane particle

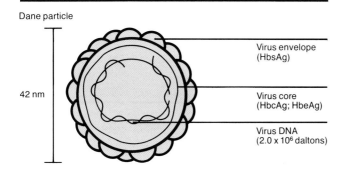

42 nm

Virus envelope
(HbsAg)

Virus core
(HbcAg; HbeAg)

Virus DNA
(2.0 x 10^6 daltons)

HbsAg particle

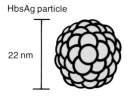

22 nm

HbsAg filament

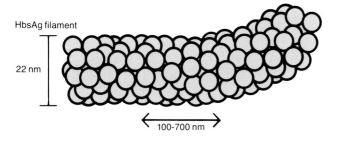

22 nm

100-700 nm

CLASSIFICATION OF VIRUSES

In the past 30 years, over 500 human viruses have been identified. Various taxonomic schemes have been proposed to group these viruses and to aid in identifying them in clinical specimens. The current and most orderly scheme, whose purpose is to reduce the large number of viruses to groups that share common features, is based on the morphology and composition of the virion. Figures 1.7a to 1.7e show classifications of the major groups of viruses, major human diseases these viruses cause, and diagrams of typical viruses in each group. Figures 1.8a to 1.8c show nucleic acid structures.

Five major criteria are used to classify viruses. In order of decreasing importance, these are (1) the nature of the nucleic acids, DNA or RNA, (2) the structure of the nucleic acid, (3) the symmetry of the nucleocapsid (icosahedral or helical), (4) the presence of a cell-derived envelope, and (5) the number of capsomers or the diameter of the helix.

Distinction of virus groups on the basis of morphologic characteristics has been suitable for classification to the level of families; however, division of families into genera is less straightforward. Most often, members within a genus share antigenicities (cross-reacting antigens) with each other but not with members of other genera. In some cases, however, genera share antigenicities. Examples are poxviruses, which are divided into genera on the basis of host range, and alphaviruses and flaviviruses, which are distinguished by the site of nucleocapsid envelopment.

Several helpful generalizations can be gleaned from Figures 1.7a to 1.7e: (1) All DNA-containing viruses except poxviruses have cubic (icosahedral) nucleocapsids; (2) of the true enveloped DNA viruses, herpesviruses and hepatitis B virus are the only classes of medical significance; (3) RNA-containing viruses can have cubic (icosahedral), helical, or unknown symmetry; and (4) RNA-containing viruses with helical or unknown symmetry are always enveloped, whereas cubic RNA viruses can be either enveloped or naked.

Figures 1.7a-1.7e. Viruses classified by structure and nucleic acid content and representative structural diagrams and related diseases.

Figure 1.7a. DNA-containing viruses with cubic (icosahedral) symmetry and naked nucleocapsids.

Figure 1.7b. DNA-containing viruses with envelopes or complex coats.

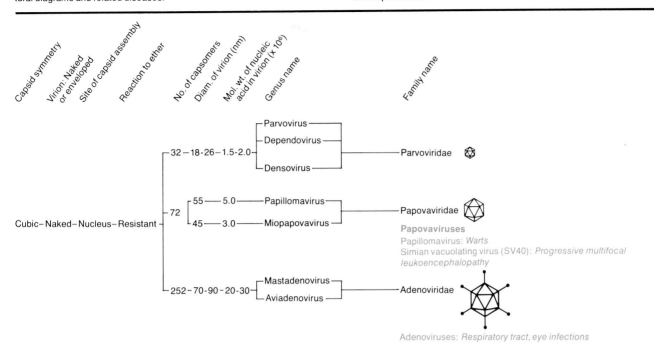

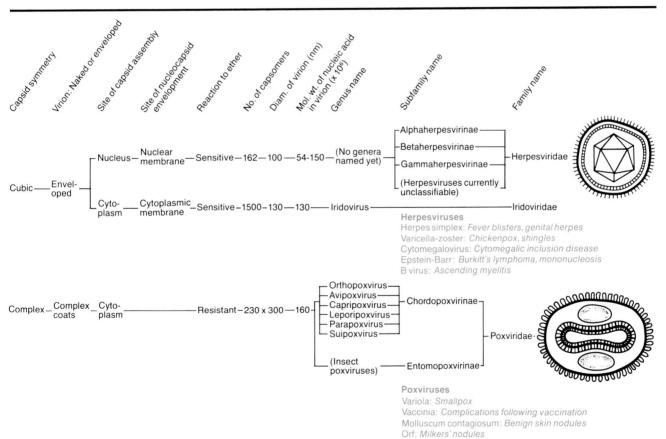

Figure 1.7c. RNA-containing viruses with cubic (icosahedral) capsid symmetry.

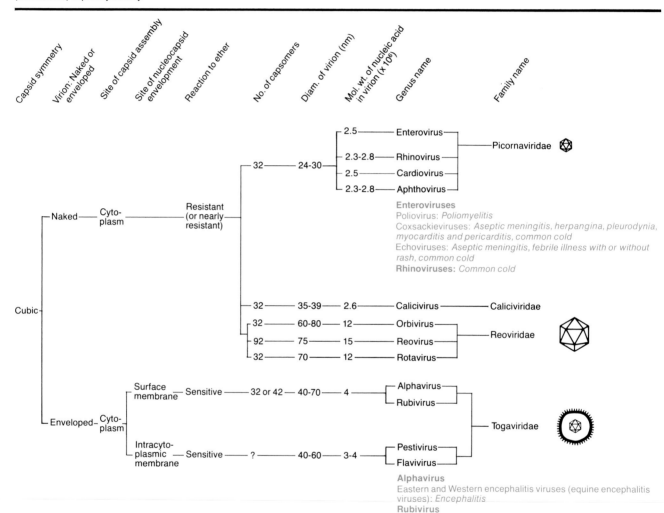

Enteroviruses
Poliovirus: *Poliomyelitis*
Coxsackieviruses: *Aseptic meningitis, herpangina, pleurodynia, myocarditis and pericarditis, common cold*
Echoviruses: *Aseptic meningitis, febrile illness with or without rash, common cold*
Rhinoviruses: *Common cold*

Alphavirus
Eastern and Western encephalitis viruses (equine encephalitis viruses): *Encephalitis*
Rubivirus
Rubella virus: *German measles*
Flavivirus
St Louis encephalitis virus: *Encephalitis*
Yellow fever virus: *Yellow fever*

Figure 1.7d. RNA-containing viruses with helical symmetry.

Figure 1.7e. RNA-containing viruses with asymmetrical or unknown architecture.

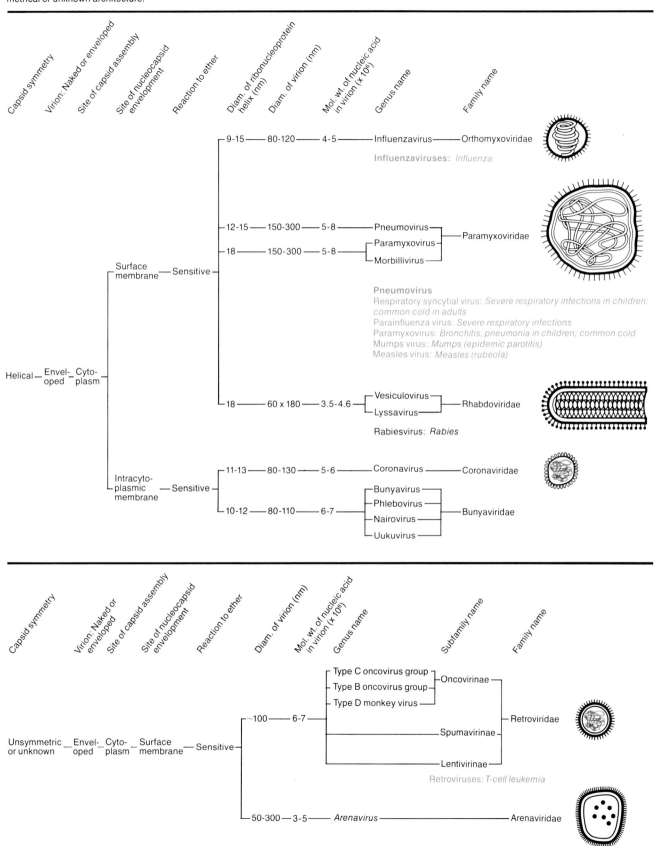

18

Figures 1.8a-1.8c. Configurations of nucleic acids.

Figure 1.8a. Configurations of DNA.

Figure 1.8b. Unusual configurations of virus DNA.

Deoxyribonucleic acid

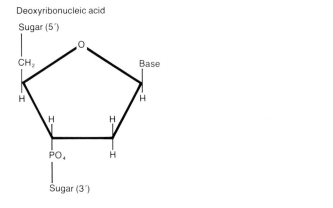

Circular DNA with both single and double stranded regions

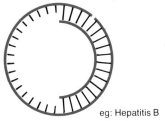

eg: Hepatitis B

Linear, double-stranded DNA containing ribonucleotides

eg: Spleen necrosis virus

Single-stranded linear

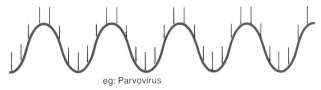

eg: Parvovirus

Double-stranded linear

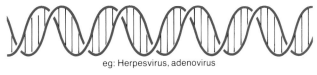

eg: Herpesvirus, adenovirus

Double-stranded circular (super coiled)

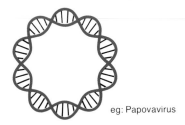

eg: Papovavirus

Selected References

Jawetz E, Melnick JL, Adelberg EA (eds): General properties of viruses, in *Review of Medical Microbiology,* ed 15. Los Altos, Calif, Lange Medical Publications, 1982, pp 323-325.

Joklik WK (ed): The structure, components and classification of viruses, in *Principles of Animal Virology.* New York, Appleton-Century-Crofts, 1980, pp 44-61.

Mathews REF: Classification and nomenclature of viruses. *Intervirology* 17:1-200, 1982.

Melnick JL: Taxonomy and nomenclature of viruses. *Prog Med Virol* 28: 208-221, 1982.

Roizman B, Carmichael LE, Deinhardt F, et al: Herpesviridae: Definition, provisional nomenclature, and taxonomy. *Intervirology* 16:201-217, 1981.

Volk WA (ed): Structure and classification of animal viruses, in *Essentials of Medical Microbiology,* ed 2. Philadelphia, JP Lippincott Co, 1982, pp 538-551.

Figure 1.8c. Configurations of RNA.

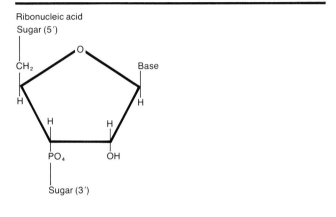

Ribonucleic acid
Sugar (5′)

Base

Sugar (3′)

Single-stranded linear

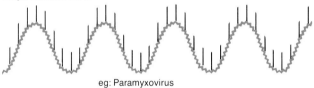

eg: Paramyxovirus

Double-stranded linear

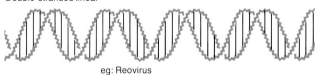

eg: Reovirus

Single-stranded circular

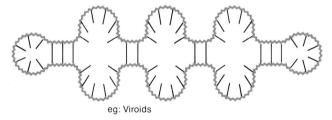

eg: Viroids

Virus
Replication

Fred Rapp, PhD

Evan Pugh Professor of Microbiology
American Cancer Society Professor of Microbiology
Professor and Chairman,
Department of Microbiology
The Milton S. Hershey Medical Center
The Pennsylvania State University
Hershey, PA 17033

PRODUCTIVE INFECTION

Animal viruses can infect a variety of cells although only very limited cell types or species will support replication of some viruses. Viral replication takes place within host cells and relies primarily on the metabolism of these cells for critical support. These characteristics distinguish viral replication from the multiplication of most other microorganisms. The replication cycle of viruses in a productive infection can be conveniently divided into eight stages (Figure 2.1): adsorption, penetration, uncoating, transcription, translation, synthesis of nucleic acids, assembly of new virus particles, and egress. In general, the same stages occur for DNA-containing and RNA-containing viruses although the events in each stage often vary.

Adsorption

The earliest interaction between a virus and a host cell is adsorption. This initial attachment of an enveloped virus to the surface of a cell occurs between glycoprotein peplomers and specific receptors on the cell surface. In the case of naked virions, the attachment takes place between specific capsid proteins and cell receptors. Different cells have receptors for different viruses, no cell has receptors for all viruses, and a cell's physiologic state may modulate its receptors. For instance, poliovirus can attach to monkey kidney cells that have been cultivated in vitro several times but not to such cells in primary cell cultures. This is because the necessary receptors are not normally present on monkey kidney cells but are acquired during culture. The adsorption of virus to cells occurs equally well at 4°C and 37°C, and adsorption is freely reversible – infectious virions can be recovered simply by shaking the culture.

Penetration

The second stage in the replication cycle is penetration. Electron microscopy indicates that viruses enter the cyto-plasm through two mechanisms. (1) Enveloped viruses penetrate the cell by fusion of the viral membrane with the cell membrane, thereby releasing the nucleocapsid directly into the cytoplasm. (2) Naked virions penetrate the cell by phagocytosis (viropexis) of the virion from the extracellular fluid; the virion resides within a vacuole, which eventually dissolves, releasing the virion into the cytoplasm. Naked virions often remain infectious until uncoating is completed a short time after penetration. Penetration proceeds very rapidly at 37°C but slowly, if at all, at 4°C. Usually at this stage, little, if any, infectious virus can be recovered.

Uncoating

Uncoating takes place in the cytoplasm where cell enzymes attack and partially remove the capsid structure. Cellular proteases uncoat all animal viruses except poxviruses. Inhibitors of protein synthesis, such as cycloheximide, do not prevent uncoating. This suggests that the cellular enzymes required for uncoating are present before virus infection occurs. Once uncoating is completed, little infectious virus can be recovered from cells.

Uncoating marks the beginning of the eclipse phase (Figure 2.2) of the replication cycle, a phase when infectious virus cannot be detected. The first three stages of the cycle are very similar for DNA and RNA viruses; however, the remaining stages diverge.

Transcription and translation of DNA-containing viruses

During the latent period (Figure 2.2), many metabolic events lead to the synthesis of new infectious virions. Virus DNA migrates to the host-cell nucleus and enters through the nuclear pores. Once inside the nucleus, virus DNA is transcribed by host-cell DNA-dependent RNA polymerase. Virus messenger RNA (mRNA) is processed in the same manner as cellular mRNA and is transported to the cytoplasm, where it is translated

Figure 2.1. Schematic representation of the replication cycle of a virus.

Figure 2.2. General replication cycle of an animal virus.

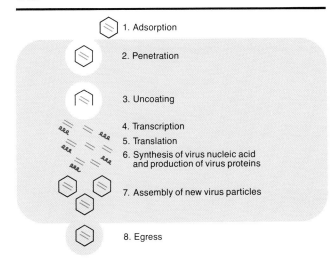

1. Adsorption

2. Penetration

3. Uncoating

4. Transcription
5. Translation
6. Synthesis of virus nucleic acid and production of virus proteins

7. Assembly of new virus particles

8. Egress

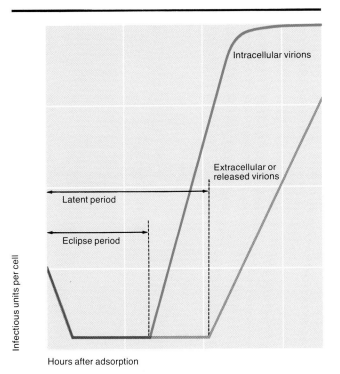

Intracellular virions

Extracellular or released virions

Latent period

Eclipse period

Infectious units per cell

Hours after adsorption

into proteins by cellular ribosomes and transfer RNA (tRNA) molecules. The transcription patterns of various DNA-containing viruses vary considerably and depend heavily on cellular enzymes in the nucleus. The viral polypeptides then migrate either to the nucleus or to cellular membranes. Some of the polypeptides that enter the nucleus are nonstructural proteins involved in the sixth stage of replication, synthesis of nucleic acid (DNA replication).

Synthesis, assembly, and egress of DNA-containing viruses

With two exceptions, the DNA-containing viruses consist of double-stranded DNA. The parvoviruses contain single linear strands of DNA, and the papovaviruses contain circular DNA. DNA replicates semiconservatively. Replication begins at one or more unique sites and proceeds bidirectionally except in the adenovirus, in which the DNA replicates unidirectionally. During DNA synthesis, capsid proteins are synthesized in the cytoplasm and migrate into the nucleus, where they aggregate into capsomers and assemble into capsids. After the capsids are formed, the DNA is inserted. The site of virion assembly for all DNA-containing viruses except the poxviruses is the host nucleus.

Like bacteria, the poxviruses replicate exclusively in the cytoplasm. Their replication probably depends on host macromolecular synthesis because they require few host enzymes. The early stages of replication are similar to those of other viruses, but extended transcription of early mRNA occurs while part of the virus membrane is still intact. Poxvirus DNA is replicated in "factories" within the cytoplasm (Figure 2.3). The DNA-synthesizing sites in the cytoplasm are Feulgen positive, a hallmark for identifying infected cells. Replication is followed by assembly and then egress of the virus particles.

The herpesviruses induce synthesis of virus-specified polypeptides, some of which migrate to cellular mem-

Figure 2.3. Replication of poxviruses.

Figure 2.4. Replication of herpesviruses.

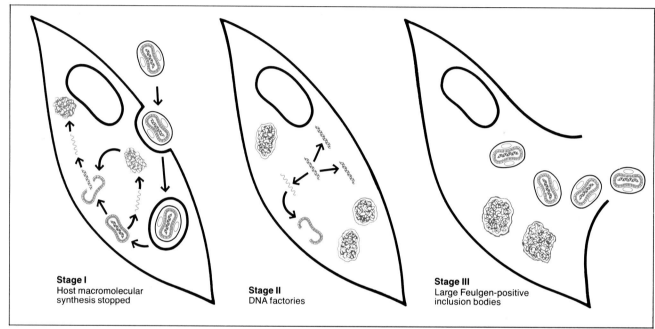

Stage I
Host macromolecular
synthesis stopped

Stage II
DNA factories

Stage III
Large Feulgen-positive
inclusion bodies

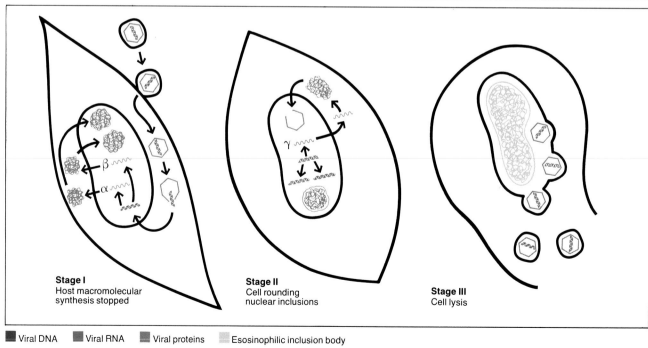

Stage I
Host macromolecular
synthesis stopped

Stage II
Cell rounding
nuclear inclusions

Stage III
Cell lysis

■ Viral DNA   ■ Viral RNA   ▦ Viral proteins   ▦ Esosinophilic inclusion body

branes, where the polypeptides are glycosylated by cellular enzymes. These sites of glycosylated proteins correspond to sites of envelopment of herpesvirus nucleocapsids and appear in electron micrographs as thickened areas. Envelopes are formed around the nucleocapsids by budding from the inner layer of the nuclear membrane. The bud detaches and is freed within the perinuclear space. Virions are then released from the cell by (1) passing through the endoplasmic reticulum to the extracellular spaces or (2) using the outer layer of the nuclear membrane to form vacuoles that contain one or more virions (Figure 2.4). Vacuoles containing the virions are then transported to the cell surface, where they release the virions. Cell lysis often follows.

Nonenveloped DNA viruses (eg, adenoviruses, papovaviruses, and parvoviruses) are synthesized until host cytopathology prevents production of new virions. The virions are released from the nucleus only when the nuclear membrane disintegrates and from the cell after the cell dies. Once intact virions are produced, infectious virus can be recovered by disrupting the cells, and the virus can be recognized by electron microscopy.

The replication of hepatitis B virus (HBV) is not yet well understood because it has not been grown in cell culture. However, its DNA has several unique features that affect virus synthesis. The DNA is a small circular molecule within the nucleocapsid of the 42nm HBV virion; the DNA has a contour length equivalent to 3200 nucleotide bases. The nucleic acid is only partially double stranded; it is composed of a long strand with a constant length of 3200 bases and a short strand that varies in different molecules from 1700 to 2800 bases. This leaves a single strand along 13% to 47% of the length of the long strand. The short strand, however, becomes elongated by a virion DNA polymerase in the nucleocapsid; and during this reaction, the DNA becomes fully double stranded. The function of a circular DNA genome that contains a variably sized, single strand that is repaired by virion DNA polymerase is unknown, but the single strand is unique among the animal viruses.

Approximately 300 bases proximal to the 5' end of the short strand, a small discontinuity is also present in the long strand. This interruption, which is not repaired by the virion DNA polymerase, allows the DNA to be converted from a circular to a linear form under conditions that selectively denature the 300-base pair region between the two 5' ends. In addition, a protein is covalently bound to the 5' end of the long strand. This protein may be an endonuclease that nicks the long strand and enables the conversion of circular HBV DNA to linear forms in vivo.

DNA viruses use only cellular enzymes to transcribe their mRNA, and DNA replication and virion assembly take place exclusively within the nucleus. The single exception is the poxvirus group, which replicates exclusively within the cytoplasm.

Transcription, translation, and synthesis of RNA-containing viruses

The adsorption, penetration, and uncoating processes of the replication cycle of most RNA-containing viruses are the same as those of DNA-containing viruses. Once released from the nucleocapsid, however, the RNA remains in the cytoplasm; and the entire replication cycle for almost all RNA-containing viruses occurs without the involvement of the nucleus. Orthomyxoviruses and retroviruses are the exceptions; these viruses do have a nuclear phase.

The introduction of RNA as genetic material poses problems for both transcription and replication of the nucleic acid. Widely diverse types of RNAs compose the genome of RNA viruses; the RNAs may be double or single stranded, composed of a single piece or segmented with several pieces of RNA needed to make up the RNA complement. In addition, the RNA within the virion may have the polarity of mRNA (positive-strand

Figure 2.5. Types of virus RNA and transcription. The numbers of multiple genome pieces or copies are only representations.

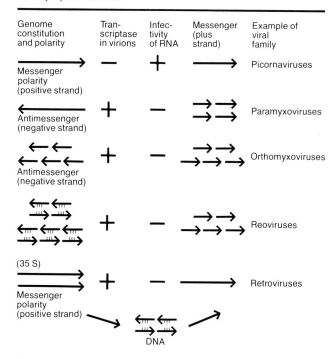

Genome constitution and polarity	Tran-scriptase in virions	Infec-tivity of RNA	Messenger (plus strand)	Example of viral family

RNA), or it may have polarity complementary to mRNA (negative-strand RNA), as shown in Figure 2.5.

Replication of a single-stranded RNA molecule requires the action of an RNA-dependent RNA polymerase. No such enzymatic activity is present in uninfected animal cells. Infected cells can acquire this activity two ways. In positive-strand viruses (Figure 2.6) except for retroviruses, the parental RNA acts directly as mRNA and is translated into the RNA-dependent RNA polymerase and into capsid proteins. The newly synthesized RNA-RNA-dependent polymerase initiates the synthesis of a complementary negative strand of RNA and the synthesis and displacement of new positive strands of RNA, some of which also act as additional copies of mRNA and some of which are encapsidated to produce new virions (Figure 2.5, picornaviruses).

The RNA of negative-strand viruses (Figure 2.5), paramyxoviruses and orthomyxoviruses (Figures 2.7 and 2.8) cannot act as mRNA. The required RNA-dependent RNA polymerase is brought into the cell by the virions. New polymerase molecules that are bound to the RNA are produced using the virus message and are incorporated into newly produced virions.

The retroviruses have a totally different method of replication. They carry the genetic information for induction of an RNA-dependent DNA polymerase (reverse transcriptase). Once reverse transcriptase has catalyzed the synthesis of double-stranded DNA complementary to the virus RNA, the virus-specified DNA moves to the nucleus; retroviruses must integrate this DNA into the host chromosome (Figure 2.9) before synthesis of new infectious virus can occur. The integrated DNA is used as a template for transcription of RNA, which is translated into required virus proteins.

Assembly and egress of RNA-containing viruses

All RNA-containing viruses except orthomyxoviruses assemble the nucleocapsid in the cytoplasm. Naked

Figure 2.6. Replication of picornaviruses and togaviruses.

Figure 2.7. Replication of paramyxoviruses and rhabdoviruses.

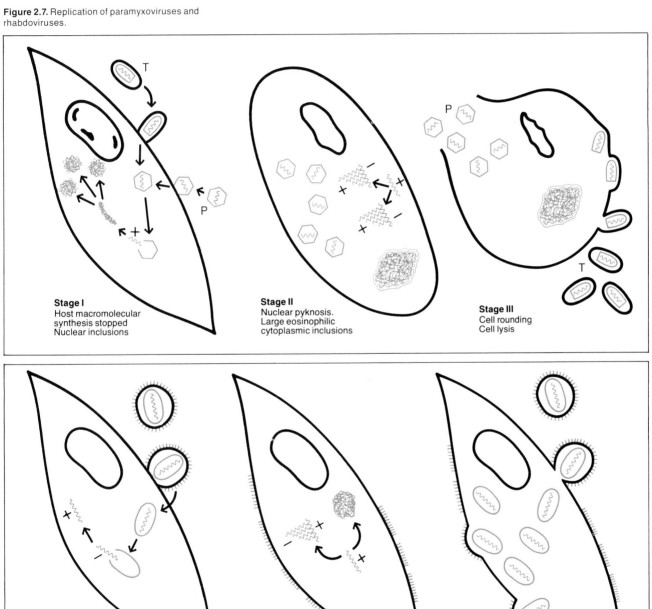

Stage I
Host macromolecular synthesis stopped Nuclear inclusions

Stage II
Nuclear pyknosis. Large eosinophilic cytoplasmic inclusions

Stage III
Cell rounding Cell lysis

Stage I

Stage II

Stage III
Cytoplasmic inclusion bodies

■ Viral DNA   ■ Viral RNA   ■ Viral proteins

28

Figure 2.8. Replication of orthomyxoviruses.

Figure 2.9. Replication of retroviruses.

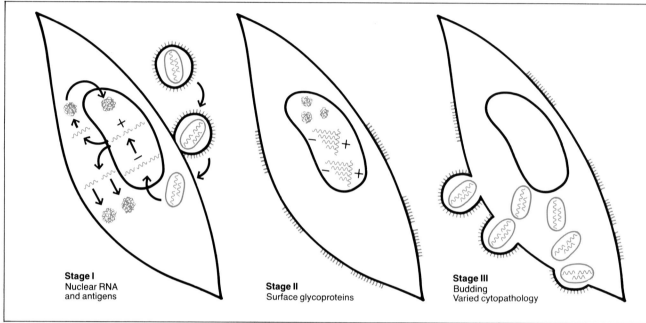

Stage I
Nuclear RNA
and antigens

Stage II
Surface glycoproteins

Stage III
Budding
Varied cytopathology

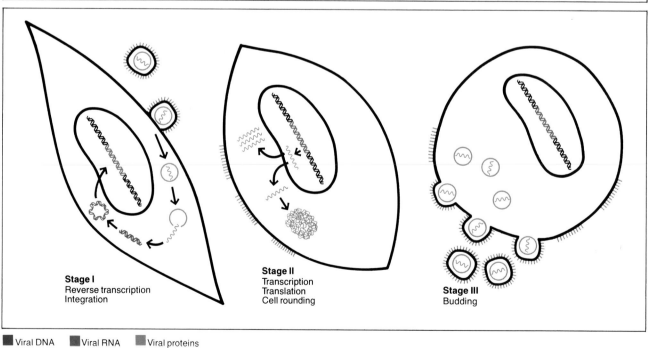

Stage I
Reverse transcription
Integration

Stage II
Transcription
Translation
Cell rounding

Stage III
Budding

■ Viral DNA   ■ Viral RNA   ■ Viral proteins

RNA-containing viruses are released from cells upon cell death. Most enveloped RNA viruses are released by budding through the plasma membrane (Figure 2.10). A patch of cell membrane that contains viral envelope proteins serves as a precursor to the envelope of the budding virion. These viral envelope proteins presumably associate with regions on the inner surface of the cell membrane. The nucleoprotein then binds specifically to the membrane in those regions, and the budding process occurs by an outfolding and pinching-off of a segment of the membrane, thus enclosing the associated nucleoprotein. Host-cell polypeptides are excluded from membrane regions that are precursors of the viral envelope, and such polypeptides are not detected in purified virus preparations. The orthomyxoviruses, paramyxoviruses, rhabdoviruses, arenaviruses, togaviruses of the alphavirus and rubivirus groups, and retroviruses bud exclusively through the plasma membrane, and all of these viruses hemadsorb (red cells attach to the membrane of infected cells). The coronaviruses and flavivirus (yellow fever) of the togavirus group bud through intracytoplasmic membranes.

Two additional points concerning the replication cycle must be recognized. First, the growth curves of each major group of viruses differ, and viruses within each group may differ markedly in the time required to complete one replication cycle. Second, the assembly of virions is very inefficient. For example, in the herpesviruses, 5% to 10% of the virus DNA molecules are encapsidated. In addition, excessive capsid protein is produced, and this overproduction leads to the localized accumulation of virus components within infected cells. These accumulated products often alter histochemical staining properties and usually produce eosinophilic or Feulgen-positive masses called inclusion bodies.

Feulgen-positive inclusions in the nucleus and margination of the chromatin are early distinguishing features of cells infected with herpesviruses (Figure 2.4).

Figure 2.10. Budding of enveloped RNA viruses.

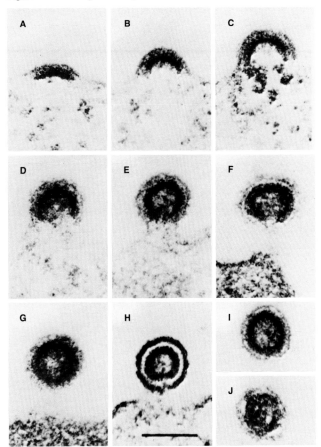

30

Figure 2.11. Outcomes of the interaction of viruses
with cells.

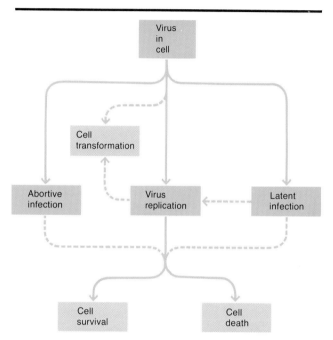

Later the inclusions, which represent a scar of virus
infection, become eosinophilic. Eosinophilic cytoplasmic inclusions in a cytomegalocyte distinguish cytomegalovirus infection.

The presence of characteristically stained inclusion
bodies may be of diagnostic significance, and the site of
inclusion bodies may be important in distinguishing
between viruses that cause similar symptoms (eg, herpes
zoster inclusion bodies are nuclear, whereas smallpox or
generalized vaccinia inclusion bodies are cytoplasmic).

ABORTIVE INFECTION

Any virus host-cell interaction that does not lead to
synthesis of new infectious virus is termed abortive
(Figure 2.11). Replication can be blocked at any step
following adsorption. If no adsorption occurs, clearly
host and virus do not interact. The consequence to the
cell may be negligible or extensive. Abortive infection
may cause cell injury and death, particularly if virus
replication interrupts host-cell metabolism. If, however,
the virus persists but does not replicate or destroy the
cell, either latent infection or transformation results.

LATENT INFECTION

A latent infection (Figure 2.11) results if the virus enters
the cell but does not immediately replicate or injure the
cell. The total genome of the virus is conserved, and
future events can trigger virus replication. This condi-
tion is important in understanding the pathogenesis of a
number of virus groups, principally the RNA-containing
retroviruses and all DNA-containing viruses other than
the poxviruses. The orthomyxoviruses may also produce
latent infections. Although reactivation of the virus can
lead to cell death, reactivation of certain viruses does
not destroy the cell harboring those latent viruses; for
example, in herpes simplex virus infection, the trigeminal
ganglion harboring the virus is not destroyed. Little is
known about the state of the virus genome in the latently

infected cell, and even less is known about the molecular events accompanying reactivation of virus synthesis.

TRANSFORMATION

Any virus-cell interaction that results in a heritable change in the cell is known as transformation (Figure 2.11). The change must be transferred to cell progeny and can be any phenotypic marker that is measurable. The interaction, therefore, does not destroy the cell, and often the recipient cells are endowed with new properties that lead to more vigorous growth, to long-term growth in culture, and frequently to malignancy.

Transformation can occur with the total virus genome complement (eg, retroviruses) or only a segment of it (eg, papovaviruses, adenoviruses, and herpesviruses). Only a few genes of the total virus genome complement are required to initiate and maintain the transformed state; recovery of infectious virus from cells harboring only a few virus genes is not feasible. Because virus DNA alone (either as total virus DNA or as fragments carrying the required gene or genes) can cause transformation, nucleic acids are the transforming unit for mammalian cells, a fact known about *bacterial* transformation since 1944.

Selected References

Bishop DH: *The Rhabdoviruses.* Boca Raton, Fla, CRC Press, 1979, vol 1.

Bishop JM: The molecular biology of RNA tumor viruses: A physician's guide. *N Engl J Med* 303:675-682, 1980.

Freeman BA (ed): The orthomyxoviruses; the paramyxoviruses; the rhabdoviruses; the RNA tumor viruses, in *Burrow's Textbook of Microbiology.* Philadelphia, WB Saunders Co, 1979, pp 990-1021.

Holowczak JA: Poxvirus DNA. *Curr Top Microbiol Immunol* 97:27-79, 1982.

Mitra S: DNA replication in viruses. *Annu Rev Genet* 14:347-397, 1980.

Putnak JR, Phillips BA: Picornaviral structure and assembly. *Microbiol Rev* 45(2):287-315, 1981.

Rapp F: Herpes simplex viruses, in Holmes K, Mardh PA, Sparling PF, Wiesner PJ (eds): *Sexually Transmitted Diseases.* New York, McGraw-Hill Book Co, to be published.

Roizman B: The organization of the herpes simplex virus genomes. *Annu Rev Genet* 13:25-57, 1979.

Siddell St, Wege H, ter Meulen V: Structure and replication of coronaviruses. *Curr Top Microbiol Immunol* 99:131-164, 1982.

Simons K, Garoff H, Helenius A: How an animal virus gets into and out of its host cell. *Sci Am* 246(2):58-66, 1982.

Cultivation and Assay of Viruses

David A. Lennette, PhD
Codirector

Evelyne T. Lennette, PhD
Codirector

Virolab, Inc
4560 Horton Street
Emeryville, CA 94608

EFFECTS AND DETECTION OF VIRUSES IN LABORATORY HOSTS

Because viruses are obligate intracellular parasites, viral cultivation requires live hosts. Several species of laboratory animals (mice, rats, and guinea pigs), embryonated chicken eggs, cultures of bits of differentiated tissue, and cell cultures are widely used; however, the suitability of each host depends on the virus to be studied.

Laboratory animals

Small laboratory animals are particularly useful for examining the pathogenicity of viruses. For example, the animals may be used to distinguish between relatively nonpathogenic attenuated-virus vaccine strains and pathogenic wild-type strains. Suckling mice, which perhaps are the most commonly used animal hosts, are useful for the recovery of viruses that will not grow in cell cultures, notably some of the group A coxsackieviruses. Mice are also useful for the isolation of rabiesvirus and lymphocytic choriomeningitis virus, both of which produce characteristic illness in these animals. Although both viruses will grow in cell cultures, such growth will not produce characteristic cytopathic effects. Mice are useful for the isolation of pathogenic togaviruses and bunyaviruses from vectors; nonpathogenic viruses and other microbes commonly found in vectors will not cause disease in inoculated animals and consequently will not interfere with isolation of pathogenic togaviruses and bunyaviruses.

Viruses are grown by using mice less than three days old when they are most susceptible to infection. The mice are inoculated with a specimen or other source of virus, and mice that die the first day after inoculation are examined to see whether they died from the trauma of inoculation. Surviving mice are examined frequently for evidence of viral infection, typical signs of which include failure to nurse (no milk visible in the stomach); changes in color or appearance; unusual activity such as excitement, torpor, or paralysis; or changes in posture.

Although infections caused by different viruses may produce similar symptoms, some viral infections produce characteristic syndromes. For example, the group A coxsackieviruses produce flaccid paralysis, whereas the group B coxsackieviruses produce tremors and spastic paralysis. Rabiesvirus most often produces tremors, paralysis, and incoordination, followed by death. If no symptoms are observed, the mice are usually kept for two weeks or longer before being killed.

Mice that exhibit symptoms of viral infection are killed and dissected to obtain tissues for further study. Histologic examination of such tissues may reveal characteristic effects of certain viruses. For example, mice infected with group A coxsackieviruses have many lesions of the voluntary muscles, but brain and fatty tissues do not have characteristic lesions. In contrast, mice infected with the group B coxsackieviruses do not have lesions of the voluntary muscles but develop evidence of encephalitis and fatty-tissue necrosis (Figures 3.1 and 3.2); these group B viruses may also produce pancreatitis and myocarditis in mice (Figures 3.3a and 3.3b) and in humans.

Embryonated chicken eggs

The embryonated chicken egg has long been widely used as a sensitive host for the cultivation of influenza viruses. Compared with laboratory animals, embryonated eggs offer several advantages: (1) They are sterile, (2) they have no developed immunologic functions, (3) they are inexpensive, and (4) they are available almost anywhere in the world. Embryonated eggs are also more suitable than cell cultures because eggs yield more influenza virus. Because the amount of virus antigen needed could not be produced in cell cultures, influenza vaccine production depends on the growth of egg-adapted vaccine strains of virus.

Influenza viruses are isolated by inoculating specimens into the allantoic and amniotic cavities of several eggs (Figure 3.4), which are then incubated for three days.

Figure 3.1. Coxsackie group B infection in mouse. Early degeneration at the margin of a fat pad represented by the band of darker cells that extend from upper left to lower right.

Figure 3.2. An early cerebral lesion showing neuronal necrosis due to coxsackie group B virus in a mouse. Cerebral lesion represented by the band of enlarged dark cells near the left center.

Figures 3.3a-3.3b. Coxsackie B3 myocarditis in Swiss-Webster mouse.

Figure 3.3a. Extensive mineralization in the myocardium of a 21-day-old mouse seven days after virus inoculation.

Figure 3.3b. Focal eosinophilic cellular necrosis in the myocardium of a 14-day-old mouse three days after infection developed.

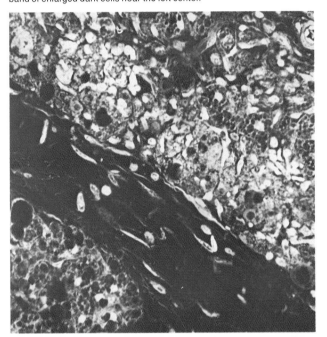
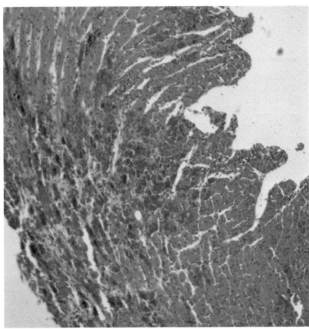
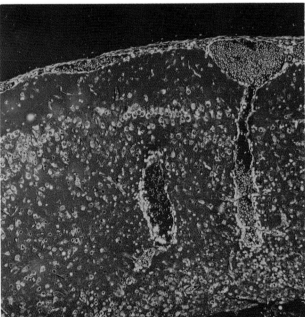
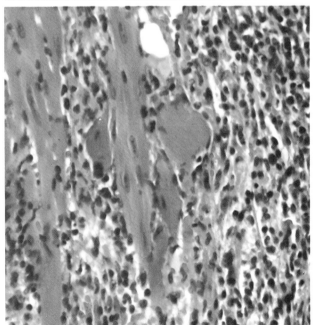

Figure 3.4. Egg inoculation techniques. *Left top:* Inoculation into the amniotic cavity of an 11-day-old chick embryo. *Left bottom:* Inoculation onto the chorioallantoic membrane of a 10-day-old chick embryo. *Right top:* Inoculation into the allantoic cavity of a 10-day-old chick embryo. *Right bottom:* Inoculation into the yolk sac of a 6-day-old chick embryo.

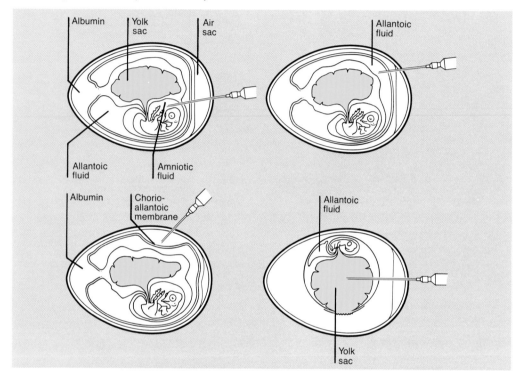

Although the viral infection may be fatal to the embryo, it is not examined for specific pathologic changes. Instead, fluids from the amniotic and allantoic cavities are collected and tested for the presence of viral hemagglutinins (virus surface proteins that cause erythrocytes to agglutinate, or clump together).

If the chorioallantoic membrane (CAM) is used as the inoculation site, quantitative assay of viruses that form lesions on the CAM is feasible. Many poxviruses produce such lesions, and experienced observers can distinguish pocks produced by different viruses, such as cowpox (Figure 3.5) and monkeypox. In fact, during the smallpox eradication campaign, vaccinia and variola viruses were often differentiated this way. Inoculation of the CAM also permits biotyping of herpes simplex viruses; lesions due to type 1 differ from those due to type 2.

Organ cultures

Certain viruses that are very difficult to isolate or propagate in cell cultures are successfully grown and recovered in so-called organ cultures (small bits of differentiated tissue maintained under conditions similar to those used for cell cultures). Organ cultures (Figure 3.6) do not grow appreciably while they are maintained in the laboratory and have a limited lifetime. Because initiation of each culture requires fresh human tissue, organ cultures are not suited for routine use, but they are important for research and special clinical studies.

For example, human coronaviruses and human rotaviruses are usually too fastidious to propagate in cell cultures but have propagated in organ cultures prepared from human fetal trachea and intestine. Coronaviruses cause both respiratory infections and enteric infections although their role in causing enteric disease is not yet established. Human rotaviruses cause diarrhea. Organ cultures used for the growth of these viruses consist of small fragments of ciliated epithelium from nasal, tracheal, or intestinal mucosa. When these cultures are properly maintained, the cilia continue to beat; viral infection of the culture may destroy or immobilize the cilia. Some coronaviruses and rotaviruses do not appear to affect the cilia, however, and must be detected by electron microscopy or immunofluorescent examination of the infected organ cultures.

Cell cultures

For most virology laboratories, cell cultures are the least expensive and most convenient means of isolation and cultivation of viruses from clinical specimens. Most of the more commonly encountered viruses grow and produce recognizable changes in cell cultures. Many of the viruses isolated in embryonated eggs or suckling mice can also be isolated in cell cultures, but many viruses that can be isolated in cell cultures cannot readily be isolated in eggs and mice. Examples are echoviruses, rubella virus, respiratory syncytial virus, adenoviruses, cytomegalovirus, and varicella-zoster virus.

Although cell cultures may be derived from many different tissues and have different characteristics, those used most widely in diagnostic virology laboratories are derived from human tissues, monkey tissues, or occasionally from tissues of a few species of small laboratory animals. The cells are grown in monolayer cultures. The selected references at the end of this chapter list sources of more detailed information about cell cultures.

Cytopathic effects (CPE) are defined as characteristic morphologic changes produced by the virus replication processes that damage infected cells. Related viruses tend to produce similar CPE, which can be distinguished from CPE produced by other virus groups. Different viruses may grow at different rates and in different types

Figure 3.5. Cowpox lesions on chorioallantoic membrane (CAM).

Figure 3.6. Organ culture of human fetus intestine.

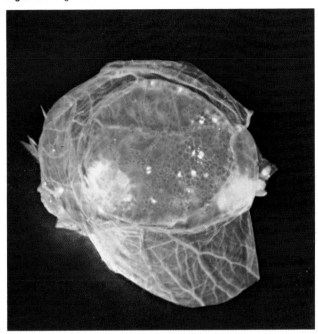

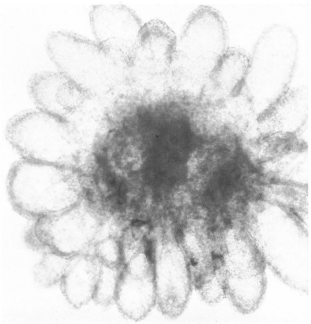

38

Figure 3.7. Rubella virus plaques in Vero cells.

Figure 3.8. Measles virus hemadsorption.

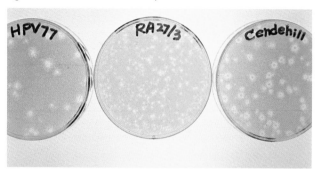

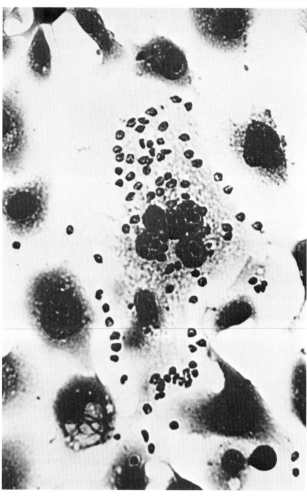

of cell cultures. Thus, the CPE can often be used with limited clinical information to preliminarily identify a newly isolated virus strain.

If infection from a single cell spreads to a small number of adjacent cells, the area of infected cells may be visible as a focus of infection. Foci may be easily recognized if the virus produces CPE in the infected cells. Even if CPE are not evident, foci may appear as plaques (Figure 3.7) or areas with altered staining properties when the cell culture is grown under a semi-solid medium prepared with agarose or another low-temperature gelling agent. The gelled medium prevents the rapid spread of viral infection to all parts of the cell culture so plaques can be counted to provide a quantitative assay.

Some viruses that readily infect and grow in cell cultures do not produce CPE, or they produce CPE only after a variable period of adaptation to growth in cell cultures. These viruses must be detected by other effects on cell cultures.

Several groups of viruses, notably the myxoviruses, paramyxoviruses, and togaviruses, induce the production of *hemagglutinins* in the cells they infect. The hemagglutinins are usually detectable earlier than the CPE if CPE are produced at all. These hemagglutinins cause the surfaces of infected cells to adhere to the erythrocytes of certain species, and this is the basis of the hemadsorption test shown in Figure 3.8. As infected host cells release newly produced virus, hemagglutinins accumulate in cell culture fluids; these fluids can then be used to demonstrate the presence of a virus because the infected cells will agglutinate the erythrocytes of appropriate species.

The Epstein-Barr virus (EBV), the common etiologic agent of infectious mononucleosis, is a herpesvirus that usually will not infect cells other than human type-B lymphocytes, which are precursors of antibody-producing plasma cells. Lymphocytes from the blood of persons who have not been infected with EBV ordinarily do not

Figure 3.9. Epstein-Barr virus-transformed lymphocytes stained by immunofluorescence for EBV nuclear antigen.

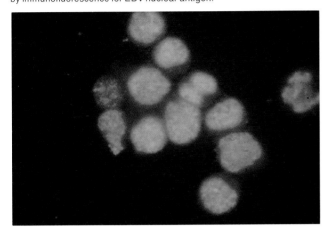

Figures 3.10a-3.10d. Various cytopathologic changes.

Figure 3.10a. Flat cervical condyloma (wart) tissue stained with hematoxylin and eosin. Note the vacuolated cells, koilocytes, in the superficial epithelium.

Figure 3.10b. Progressive multifocal leukoencephalopathy. *Left:* Discrete early demyelinating lesion with astrocytic giant cell (close to center), oligodendrocytes with enlarged hyperchromatic nuclei (along periphery), and regularly sized oligodendrocytes with surrounding intact white matter (luxol-fast blue stain for myelin; cresyl-violet stain for nuclei). Virus particles are found mainly in the enlarged oligodendroglial nuclei. *Right:* Giant astrocytes — one in mitosis, pathognomonic oligodendrocyte (arrow), and scattered macrophages. Hematoxylin and eosin stains.

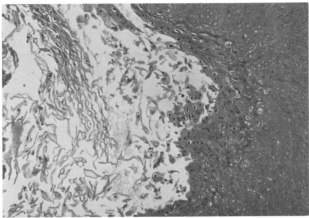

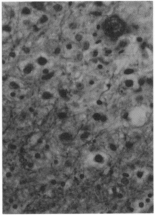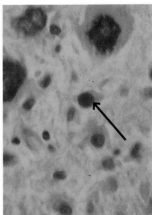

persist longer than a few weeks in cell culture. However, after infection with EBV, these cells become transformed and will grow and divide indefinitely in cell culture. EBV-infected lymphocytes maintained in cell culture do not develop CPE, but the infection can be identified by demonstrating EBV antigens and DNA in the cells. EBV-infected lymphocytes stained to detect EBV nuclear antigen are shown in Figure 3.9.

Some viruses prevent or *interfere* with the growth of other viruses in cell cultures. For example, a cell culture suspected of being infected with rubella virus, which does not produce distinctive CPE in most cell cultures, can be challenged with a small quantity of enterovirus, usually echovirus type 11. If rubella virus infection is present, the challenge enterovirus will not grow, and no CPE will develop. This method of detecting virus infection is somewhat time-consuming and not widely used when other methods are available.

DIRECT DETECTION OF VIRUSES
Cytopathology
One of the oldest laboratory methods to detect viral infections was to find characteristic cytologic changes in tissues affected by the infection. Several types of changes are associated with viral infections and may be quite

useful diagnostically, but such changes may occur in conditions other than viral infections. More than one may be associated with a single infection. Examples of cytologic changes are listed below and shown in Figures 3.10a to 3.10d.

Necrosis of target cells in viral infections may serve as a useful clue to the etiologic agent. For example, in poliomyelitis, the anterior horn cells of the spinal cord characteristically become necrotic; in genital herpes simplex infections, only mucosal squamous epithelium is destroyed.

Several types of inclusion bodies characterize par-

Figure 3.10c. Stained herpes simplex encephalitis brain tissue.

Figure 3.10d. Stained molluscum contagiosum (poxvirus) tissue.

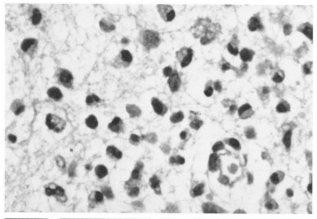

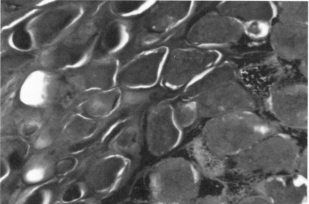

ticular viral infections. For example, infections with herpesviruses, adenoviruses, and papovaviruses produce intranuclear inclusions, but infections with rabiesvirus, poxviruses, and cytomegalovirus (CMV) produce cytoplasmic inclusions.

Syncytia, which appear microscopically as masses of multinucleate giant cells, are characteristic of several viral infections, such as those produced by measles, herpes simplex, and the parainfluenza viruses. Cytomegaly, or enlargement of infected cells, occurs with adenovirus and cytomegalovirus infections.

Immunospecific staining

Rapid immunospecific staining, by either immunofluorescence or immunoperoxidase (enzyme-linked) methods, can be applied both to the identification of a virus isolated in cell culture and to the detection of viral antigens in cells obtained directly from clinical specimens (direct detection). With immunofluorescent staining, rubella virus can be identified in cell culture. Immunofluorescent staining is considerably faster and easier than the interference test. In addition, the immunofluorescent stain provides final identification of the isolate, but the interference test demonstrates only the presence of a noncytopathic virus which may not be rubella virus.

Although immunofluorescent identification of viral isolates is useful and rapid, immunofluorescent methods are most valuable for direct demonstration of viruses in clinical specimens and rapid diagnosis of viral infection. Immunospecific staining (Figures 3.11 and 3.12) procedures may eliminate the need to isolate the virus in cell cultures. Several common immunofluorescent staining methods are in use, and each has some advantages; all are useful when carried out with good quality reagents and appropriate controls.

The enzyme-linked staining procedures are referred to as immunoperoxidase (IP) methods because peroxidase is the only enzyme commonly used for cytologic stain-

41

Figure 3.11. Immunofluorescent staining. *Top:* Measles virus antigen in the superficial epithelium and in the connective tissue stained with hyperimmune rabbit antiserum to measles virus conjugated with fluorescein isothiocyanate (FITC). *Bottom:* Varicella virus antigen in a papular skin lesion stained with hyperimmune monkey antiserum to varicella virus conjugated with FITC.

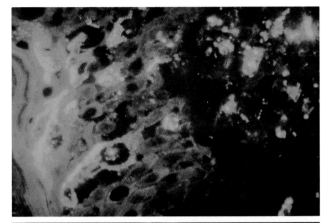
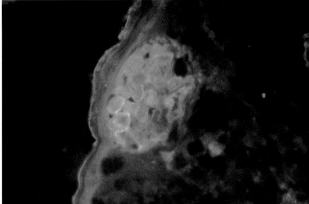

Figure 3.12. Immunofluorescent staining methods.

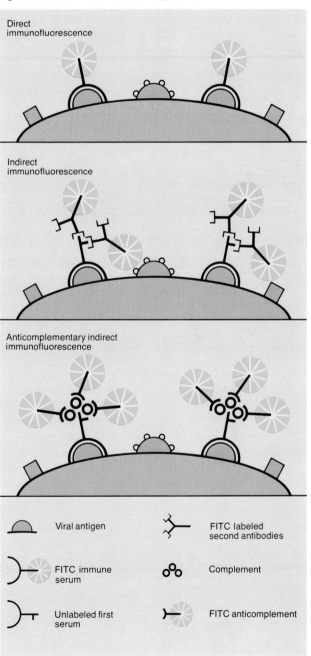

Direct immunofluorescence

Indirect immunofluorescence

Anticomplementary indirect immunofluorescence

Viral antigen

FITC immune serum

Unlabeled first serum

FITC labeled second antibodies

Complement

FITC anticomplement

Figure 3.13. Immunoperoxidase staining methods.

Figure 3.14. Immunofluorescent staining of rabies virus in olfactory nerve terminal.

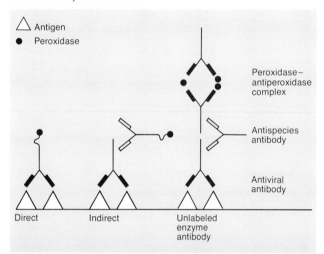

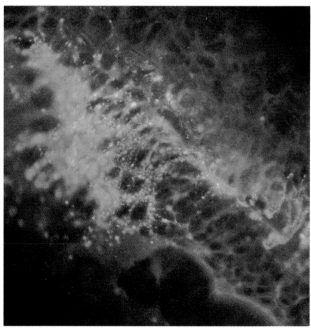

ing. The IP methods are essentially equivalent to the immunofluorescent (IF) methods, but the IP methods result in a more permanently stained preparation. IP staining procedures are shown in Figure 3.13.

For any IF or IP test to be successful, the quality and quantity of the test specimen must be adequate. The most commonly encountered problems are (1) failure to obtain an adequate number of cells for examination and (2) failure to obtain a specimen from a site likely to yield infected cells. Rapid diagnosis by IP and IF methods is also restricted to viral infections for which the number of suspected viruses is small and suitable reagents are available. For example, enteroviral infections require too large a number of reagents to cover all possible virus types; however, confirmation of suspected cytomegalovirus pneumonia in an immunosuppressed patient is entirely feasible.

One widespread use of immunofluorescence as a rapid diagnostic method is the direct immunofluorescent examination of brain tissue for diagnosis of rabies in both animals and man. This remarkably reliable test is more sensitive than tests involving the inoculation of infant mice and has even been used successfully to detect rabies antigens in the tissues of animals exhumed a week or more after burial! One example of IF staining of rabies virus antigens is shown in Figure 3.14.

Figures 3.15a to 3.15c show the effects of various immunofluorescent stains and filters on a section of a mouse pancreas infected with reovirus.

Enzyme immunoassays

Enzyme-linked immunoassay (EIA) methods are suitable for the detection of free (not cell-associated) viral antigens. Specimens from patients with a few viral diseases may contain an adequate quantity of such antigens. The utility of EIA tests for rapid diagnosis of viral diseases is the subject of much research, and some of the results are very encouraging. For example, a "sandwich"

43

Figures 3.15a-3.15c. Effects of different immunofluorescent stains on the same tissue.

Figure 3.15a. Immunofluorescent stains of section of mouse pancreas five days after infection with reovirus. When viewed through fluorescein filters, cells containing viral antigens appear green.

Figure 3.15b. Immunofluorescent stains of section of mouse pancreas five days after infection with reovirus. When viewed through rhodamine filters, insulin-containing beta cells in the islets of Langerhans appear orange.

Figure 3.15c. Immunofluorescent stains of section of mouse pancreas five days after infection with reovirus. By double-exposure photography, insulin-containing beta cells infected with reovirus appear orange and green (or yellow).

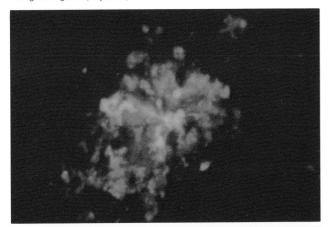

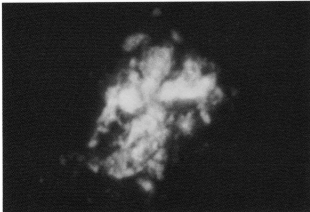

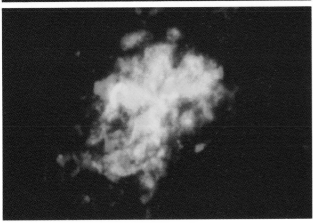

type solid-phase EIA is already widely used for rapid diagnosis of rotavirus infections; commercially available reagents are used to test stool specimens for free rotavirus. The test can be completed in five hours, qualifying it as a rapid diagnostic method. Other EIA methods may provide rapid detection of influenza virus in nasal washes. The sensitivity of EIA methods compares favorably with that of standard methods of virus isolation.

During the next few years, direct rapid methods probably will be developed to diagnose any viral infections that yield sufficient antigens in clinical specimens. Because cytomegalovirus infections commonly trouble many patients who are immunosuppressed because of disease, transplantation, or chemotherapy, investigators are currently interested in the possibility of using EIA methods to detect cytomegalovirus in clinical specimens. This would be particularly useful if antiviral therapy is developed for control of CMV infections.

Electron microscopy

Electron microscopy (EM) has a limited but important role in the detection of viruses. Electron microscopy is a good method for detecting previously undetected viruses, especially those that do not grow in usual laboratory hosts. Human viruses that were first detected by electron microscopy include most of the more recently discovered enteric viruses, including hepatitis A virus; the rotaviruses; Norwalk viruses; various enteric coronaviruses and adenoviruses; and Creutzfeldt-Jakob type papovaviruses, which may cause progressive multifocal leukoencephalopathy.

Preparation of fluid specimens for electron microscopy examination is not difficult. However, the time spent at the microscope searching for virus particles is very costly. Negative specimens require the most time! Consequently, once a virus has been characterized by electron microscopy, finding easier, less expensive methods for routine detection is important.

Selected
References

Benjamin DR: Immunoenzymatic methods, in Lennette EH, Schmidt NJ (eds): *Diagnostic Procedures for Viral, Rickettsial, and Chlamydial Infections,* ed 5. Washington, DC, American Public Health Association, 1979, pp 153-170.

Berg RA, Rennard SI, Murphy BR, et al: New enzyme immunoassays for measurement of influenza A/Victoria/3/75 virus in nasal washes. *Lancet* 1:851-853, 1980.

Caul ED, Egglestone SI: Further studies on human enteric coronaviruses. *Arch Virol* 54:107-117, 1977.

Chernesky MA: The role of electron microscopy in diagnostic virology, in Lennette DA, Specter S, Thompson KD (eds): *Diagnosis of Viral Infections: The Role of the Clinical Laboratory.* Baltimore, University Park Press, 1979, pp 125-142.

Cooper PD: The plaque assay of animal viruses, in Maramorosch K, Koprowski H (eds): *Methods in Virology.* New York, Academic Press Inc, 1967, vol 3, pp 243-311.

Craighead JE: Cytopathology in diagnostic virology, in Lennette DA, Specter S, Thompson KD (eds): *Diagnosis of Viral Infections: The Role of the Clinical Laboratory.* Baltimore, University Park Press, 1979, pp 143-158.

Dalldorf G: The coxsackie viruses. *Bull NY Acad Med* 26:329-335, 1950.

Dolin R, Blacklow NR, Malmgren RA, et al: Establishment of human fetal intestinal organ cultures for growth of viruses. *J Infect Dis* 122:227-231, 1970.

Emmons RW, Riggs JL: Application of immunofluorescence to diagnosis of viral infections, in Maramorosch K, Koprowski H (eds): *Methods in Virology.* New York, Academic Press Inc, 1977, vol 6, pp 1-28.

Flewett TH, Bryden AS, Davies H: Diagnostic electron microscopy of faeces. *J Clin Pathol* 27:603-614, 1974.

Hawkes RA: General principles underlying laboratory diagnosis of viral infections, in Lennette EH, Schmidt NJ (eds): *Diagnostic Procedures for Viral, Rickettsial, and Chlamydial Infections,* ed 5. Washington, DC, American Public Health Association, 1979, pp 42-48.

Lyerla HC: Diagnostic applications of immunofluorescence tests in the virology laboratory, in Lennette DA, Specter S, Thompson KD (eds): *Diagnosis of Viral Infections: The Role of the Clinical Laboratory.* Baltimore, University Park Press, 1979, pp 103-113.

Maramorosch K, Hirumi H (eds): *Practical Tissue Culture Applications.* New York, Academic Press Inc, 1979.

Nakano JH: Poxviruses, in Lennette EH, Schmidt NJ (eds): *Diagnostic Procedures for Viral, Rickettsial, and Chlamydial Infections,* ed 5. Washington, DC, American Public Health Association, 1979, pp 257-308.

Notkins AL, Yoon JW, Onodera T, et al: Virus induced diabetes mellitus, in Pollard M (ed): *Perspectives in Virology XI.* New York, Alan R Liss Inc, 1981.

Schmidt NJ: Cell culture techniques for diagnostic virology, in Lennette EH, Schmidt NJ (eds): *Diagnostic Procedures for Viral, Rickettsial, and Chlamydial Infections,* ed 5. Washington, DC, American Public Health Association, 1979, pp 65-139.

Schmidt NJ, Dennis J, Lennette EH: Plaque reduction neutralization test for human cytomegalovirus based upon enhanced uptake of neutral red by virus-infected cells. *J Clin Microbiol* 4:61-66, 1976.

Shelokov A, Vogel JE, Chi L: Hemadsorption (adsorption-hemmagglutination) test for viral agents in tissue culture with special reference to influenza. *Proc Soc Expt Biol Med* 97:802-809, 1958.

Yolken RH, Stopa PJ: Enzyme-linked fluorescence assay: Ultrasensitive solid-phase assay for detection of human rotavirus. *J Clin Microbiol* 10:317-321, 1979.

ZuRhein GM, Chou SM: Particles resembling papovaviruses in human cerebral demyelinating disease. *Science* 148:1477-1479, 1965.

Viral Pathogenesis and Host Resistance to Infection

Dale A. Stringfellow, PhD

Formerly Research Head, Cancer Research
Experimental Biology Research
The Upjohn Company
Kalamazoo, MI 49001

The purpose of this chapter is to provide an understanding of the interactions between viral pathogenesis and host defenses. Although people are exposed to viruses each day, the viruses cause disease in any one person only occasionally. Simplistically, this phenomenon can be attributed to a delicate balance that exists between a virus's ability to produce disease (virulence) and the host's ability to defend itself (host defenses), as shown in Figure 4.1. The host's ability to defend itself varies, which may partially account for the host's inconsistent susceptibility to disease. For example, persons who already have an infection, or who have been receiving immunosuppressive chemotherapy, or who are psychologically stressed appear to be particularly susceptible.

An understanding of the pathogenesis of a virus can provide clues as to which host defenses are necessary for protection against that specific virus. How does the virus enter the body? Where does viral replication occur? How does the virus spread to other sites of the body? How is viral pathogenesis combated? What protective role does circulating antibody play? The importance of these and other questions is illustrated by a virus that replicates only at the primary site of infection. The course and eventual outcome of such an infection are not affected by high levels of circulating antibody because the virus remains localized and does not rely on hematogenous spread (eg, influenza). Conversely, a virus that replicates at the primary site of infection may also enter the blood or lymphatic system and produce infection in other tissues of the body (eg, poliovirus). If antibody is circulating, it may inhibit viral spread from the local site. These and other interactions between viral pathogenesis and host defenses will be described.

VIRAL PATHOGENESIS

First, the virus must enter the host. Of a variety of possible portals of entry, the most common are the upper respiratory tract (inhalation), gastrointestinal tract (ingestion), mucous membranes or open wounds (direct contact with infected material), and direct injection by insect vectors. Various infections associated with these portals of entry are discussed in other chapters; however, examples of each are listed in Table 4.1.

Once in the body, the virus must find cells that not only accommodate its attachment with specific receptor sites but also support its replication. If the virus penetrates the cell, viral replication begins (Figure 2.1). A simplistic schema of viral pathogenesis is shown in Figure 4.2.

Because the host presents many obstacles, or defenses, large quantities of virus may be needed to produce infection. This phenomenon becomes particularly evident when attempts are made to transmit an upper respiratory tract infection among experimental animals. If a mouse infected with PR-8 influenza virus is put into a cage with uninfected mice, the infection will not be

Table 4.1.
Examples of the pathogenesis of specific virus infections

Virus	Portal of entry	Spread by	Target organ	Disease
Enterovirus (Polio)	Gastrointestinal tract (Ingestion)	Bloodstream	Brain	Poliomyelitis
Togavirus (Eastern equine encephalitis)	Injection site (Mosquito vector)	Bloodstream	Brain	Encephalitis
Rhinovirus	Upper respiratory tract (Inhalation)	Not systemically spread	Upper respiratory tract	Common cold
Herpes simplex virus 1	Mucous membranes (Direct contact)	Nerve route	Cutaneous tissue	Cold sores (Recurring disease)

47

Figure 4.1. Balance between viral pathogenesis
and host defenses.

Figure 4.2. Viral pathogenesis.

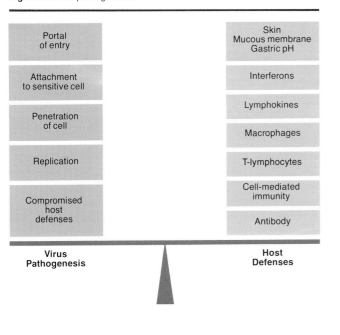

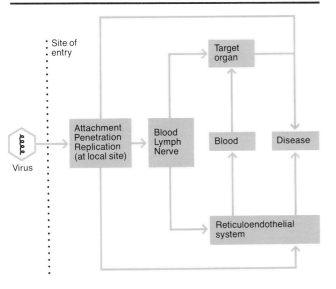

transmitted to all or even most mice. This is generally
the case with most naturally transmitted viruses.

Nevertheless, the reverse can also be true. If, for example, a young pig infected intranasally with pseudorabies virus is added to a colony of uninfected animals,
80% to 90% of the pigs will become infected. Sendai
virus is another easily transmittable virus found in most
mouse colonies. Generally, injecting virus into a host
produces infection more efficiently and with less virus
than exposing the host to an infected animal.

After the virus enters the host, penetrates the cell, and
replicates at the initial site of infection, it may or may
not cause disease at this site. Rhinoviruses are examples
of viruses that replicate at the site of entry and cause
localized disease. Viruses may also enter the blood or
lymphatic system or nerve tissues and spread to other
tissues and organs that become secondary sites of infection. At these sites, viral replication may produce cellular destruction and physiologic evidence of disease.
Togaviruses, which are transmitted by mosquito vectors,
are examples of viruses that replicate at the site of entry,
subcutaneous tissue, then spread hematogenously to
the vascular endothelium of the brain, where viral replication again occurs. The virus then crosses the blood-
brain barrier and causes encephalitis. Herpes simplex
virus is unusual in that it apparently can spread by way
of nerve tissue. Evidence of this is seen in experiments
involving mice infected intravaginally with herpes simplex virus. After viral replication at the primary site, the
virus spreads through nerve tissue to the spinal cord
and finally to brain tissue, where subsequent viral replication results in encephalitis and death.

Viral pathogenesis is often more subtle. Herpesviruses
(eg, varicella-zoster virus, herpes simplex, and cytomegalovirus) not only produce infections at primary or secondary sites but also may become dormant for prolonged
periods, only to cause disease later. A good example is
varicella-zoster virus, which may cause chickenpox in

a child. Up to 50 or 60 years later, the same virus may produce shingles (herpes zoster) in the same patient.

Reactivation of the virus may be associated with stress, immunosuppression, or another mechanism of impaired resistance in the patient. Herpes simplex virus also is usually dormant, but periodic reactivation is evidenced by the appearance of cold sores and genital lesions at the same sites affected during the initial infection. While dormant, the virus is sequestered in ganglia.

Because different patterns of viral pathogenesis require different approaches to disease prevention, diagnosis, and treatment, an understanding of how the host defends itself against viral infection is necessary.

HOST DEFENSES

Both nonspecific and specific host defenses combat viruses as well as other infectious agents. Nonspecific defenses protect against a wide variety of organisms, whereas a specific defense protects against a specific organism. Host defenses can be further categorized as physical, cellular, or humoral (Table 4.2).

Nonspecific physical defenses

Nonspecific physical defenses either prevent the virus from entering the host, or they destroy or neutralize it. Examples are skin, nasal secretions, tears, mucous membranes, and the acidity of the stomach.

Nonspecific cellular defenses

Nonspecific cellular defenses include a variety of cells ordinarily involved in the immune process. Examples are macrophages and natural killer cells, which nonspecifically identify, attack, and destroy cells recognized as foreign, such as virus-infected and neoplastic (transformed) cells.

Nonspecific humoral defenses

Nonspecific humoral defenses include substances such as interferons and lymphokines. Interferons, a group of low-molecular-weight proteins produced by cells, prevent intracellular virus replication in otherwise susceptible cells (Figure 4.3, Table 4.3). They affect a wide variety of both DNA- and RNA-containing viruses.

When sensitized lymphocytes attach to a specific antigen, they release lymphokines, such as migration inhibitory factor (MIF), chemotactic factors, blastogenic-mitogenic factors, and some types of interferons. MIF induces macrophages that are near the antigen to remain in the area, where they are stimulated to increase granule formation. The granules contain hydrolytic enzymes that help destroy invading organisms and may kill surrounding tissue cells. Chemotactic factors attract phagocytes and other host defense cells to the area. Blastogenic-mitogenic factors, such as interleukin 1 or 2, induce lymphocytes to multiply, thus providing a greatly increased number of sensitized lymphocytes.

Specific physical defenses

Specific physical defenses, ie, directed toward a specific virus, have not been identified.

Specific cellular defenses

Specific cellular defenses are produced when T-lymphocytes, or thymocytes, are sensitized (exposed) to a specific virus or viral antigen. Upon reexposure, these sensitized cells recognize the virus or viral antigen and respond anamnestically. If the antigen is on the surface of a virus-infected cell, the sensitized T-lymphocyte is attracted to the infected cell and facilitates killing of that cell. This may be accomplished by direct attachment, release of cytotoxin molecules, or release of chemoattractants, which attract additional defense cells (eg, macrophages) that kill the infected cell. Elimination of infected cells is one method of limiting viral replication. This type of sensitization is specific in that activation by one virus (eg, herpes simplex virus) does not provide im-

Table 4.2.
Examples of host defenses against viral infection

	Physical	Cellular	Humoral
Nonspecific resistance	Skin, tears, mucus, stomach acidity	Macrophages, natural killer cells	Interferons, lymphokines
Specific	None	T-lymphocytes	Circulating antibodies (IgM, IgG), local antibodies (IgA)

Table 4.3.
Properties of interferons

Low-molecular-weight proteins (many are glycoproteins): 15,000 to 30,000 molecular weight.

Three general categories: α(leukocyte-induced), β(fibroblast-induced), and γ(immune-induced). Each is distinguishable by antigenicity, amino acid composition, and molecular weight. May be more than one molecular species in each group. For example, there are an estimated 10 to 20 human α-interferons.

Inhibit virus replication through an intracellular effect that requires cellular synthesis of both new RNA and protein.

Usually stable over a broad pH range (2 to 11) and at temperatures up to 60°C for 1 hour, but stability depends on the type of interferon and its purity (more pure = less stable).

Inhibit the replication of a wide range of unrelated viruses.

Most active in cells from homologous species (species specificity) although there are exceptions with most interferons.

Limited duration of antiviral effect. After exposure to interferon, cells can be resistant for a few hours to a few days, depending on conditions.

Figure 4.3. Mechanism of action of interferons.

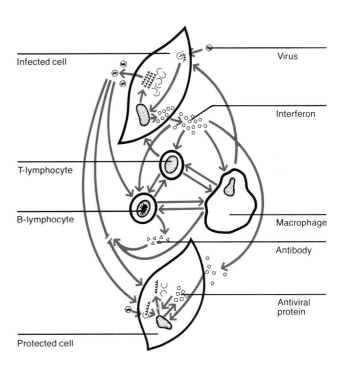

munity to another unrelated virus (eg, vaccinia virus), even though cellular immunity may play an important role in defense against both viruses.

Specific humoral defenses
Specific humoral defenses include B-lymphocytes, which produce circulating (IgG and IgM) and local (IgA) antibodies in response to exposure to foreign antigens. These antibodies, which can neutralize the infectivity of specific viruses, provide host resistance to the disease or aid in host recovery.

The role that each of these host defenses plays in providing resistance to disease depends on the pathogenesis of the invading organism. For example, the humoral immune response (IgG, IgM) may combat a systemic disease more than an upper respiratory tract infection. A virus involved in an upper respiratory tract infection may not depend on hematogenous spread and may remain restricted to the initial site of infection. In this case, circulating antibody does not defend the host against the illness; however, local antibody levels (IgA) in nasal secretions may be more important for host defense. Conversely, circulating antibody may play a significant role if the infecting virus is spread hematogenously from the initial site of infection. For example, poliovirus initially replicates in the gastrointestinal tract, and togaviruses initially replicate at the site of injection and then are transmitted through the bloodstream to susceptible target tissues. If hematogenous viral transmission is blocked by antibody that neutralizes the virus before it reaches secondary tissues, infection is curtailed.

To be pathogenic, many viruses depend on specific routes of transmission. Some viruses infect laboratory animals only after systemic injection. Cells capable of supporting viral replication must be available at the site of viral entry. If they are not, various host defenses may eliminate the virus before it reaches susceptible cells.

Although host defenses usually aid in disease resistance and recovery, the reverse can also be true. Immune responses may damage tissues or organs. During viral replication, specific viral antigens expressed on the surface of cells alter the antigenicity of those cells. Host defenses may recognize the cells as foreign and respond by destroying them, even though the infecting virus would not have destroyed them. This host-mediated cellular destruction may be manifested as disease or even death, depending on the role the cells play in homeostasis.

The classic example of this phenomenon occurs with *lymphocytic choriomeningitis* (LCM) virus infection in mice (Figure 4.4). In immunocompetent mice, LCM virus injected intracranially produces acute, fatal chorio-

meningitis; but if the virus is injected intraperitoneally, an acute infection without central nervous system (CNS) side effects occurs. These mice recover and are immune to reinfection. Cyclophosphamide, an immunosuppressant injected three days after LCM virus is injected intracranially, suppresses the immune response; consequently, the mice do not die. However, if these immunosuppressed mice receive spleen cells from immune mice six to eight days later, choriomeningitis develops; and the mice die. In the immunocompromised mouse, disease is not apparent because the virus does not destroy the infected cells. When disease does result, it is due to cellular destruction caused by the mouse's immune response, T-lymphocytes destroying CNS tissue.

Many researchers believe that some of the slowly progressing or latent CNS diseases, such as multiple sclerosis, may be manifestations of such a phenomenon in humans although proof of viral or immune-induced etiologies for most such diseases is still lacking.

THE IMMUNOCOMPROMISED HOST
The immunocompromised host has disorders of the cellular or humoral immune responses and as a result is often more susceptible to infection. An understanding of such disorders and their underlying basis may provide a better understanding of the importance of various host defenses in resistance to and recovery from viral infections.

Impaired cell-mediated immunity associated with thymic hypoplasia of certain congenital (eg, DiGeorge's syndrome) or hereditary (eg, Nezelof's syndrome) disorders produces increased susceptibility to herpesvirus infections by disrupting normal macrophage and T-lymphocyte activity, both of which play a central role in resistance to herpesvirus infections. In patients who have impaired cellular immunity and who receive vaccinia virus (smallpox) vaccine, severe localized cellular distribution and in some cases generalized cellular CNS

Figure 4.4. Lymphocytic choriomeningitis (LCM) virus infection in mice, a model of virus-induced autoimmune disease. (a) LCM virus injected intracranially in immunocompetent mice produces acute, fatal choriomeningitis. (b) LCM virus injected intraperitoneally produces acute infection without CNS side effects. Animals that recover are immune. (c) Mice injected with cyclophosphamide three days after LCM virus is injected become immunosuppressed and do not die; six to eight days after these mice receive spleen cells from immune mice, choriomeningitis develops, and the mice die. (Classic experiment of Gilden, Cole, and Nathanson.)

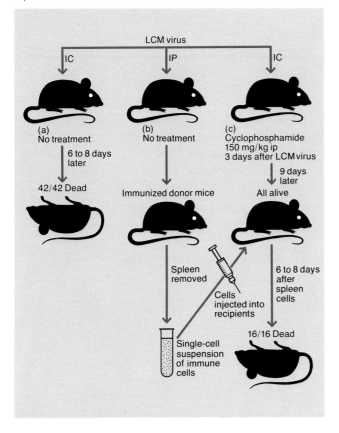

destruction occurs as a result of unrestricted viral replication. These patients have a high incidence of secondary sequelae.

Because of the potential interplay of the many components of the immune system, results of studies concerning compromised immunity must be cautiously interpreted. Although most congenital or hereditary disorders with detrimental effects on cell-mediated immunity may predominantly affect specific cell populations, other cell populations may be indirectly affected. For example, impaired macrophage function may compromise the response of both T-lymphocytes and B-lymphocytes to specific antigens or mitogenic stimuli.

The mere lack of a particular cell type may compromise immunity, but other types of cells may compensate for the lack by playing a stronger role in host defense. An example of this compensation is seen in nude mice that lack functional T-lymphocytes but have a greater-than-normal component of natural killer cells.

Other conditions that can affect one or more components of the host defense system include malnutrition, diabetes, uremia, pregnancy, age, surgery, anesthesia, drug addiction, and the use of immunosuppressive drugs. Influenza, for example, generally affects the elderly most severely; however, for unknown reasons during the influenza epidemic of 1918 to 1919, deaths occurred primarily in persons 20 to 30 years old, normally the healthiest segment of the population.

Data suggest that not all host defenses play a critical role in resistance to all viruses. The antibody response may be less important in resistance to viruses of the herpes, pox, and measles groups than in resistance to other viral infections. This reduced importance appears to be particularly likely with herpes simplex virus infection, which recurs in the presence of circulating antibody.

SUMMARY

Many questions concerning viral pathogenesis and host resistance to infection are unanswered. Why some viruses are more pathogenic than others or why different strains of the same virus have different pathogenicities is not clear. Nor are all the mechanisms of host defense or the wide variations in susceptibility clearly understood.

The development of antiviral chemotherapy depends on knowledge of the mechanisms by which the host defends itself against various viral infections as well as the mechanisms by which viruses cause disease. The characteristics and pathogenesis of both primary and secondary (if applicable) stages of disease and the disease potential of latent viral infections must be considered.

Selected
References

Fenner F, McAuslan B, Mims C, et al: *The Biology of Animal Viruses.* New York, Academic Press Inc, 1974.

Fudenberg H, Stites D, Caldwell J, et al: *Basic and Clinical Immunology.* Los Altos, Calif, Lange Medical Publications, 1980.

Gilden DH, Cole GA, Nathanson N: Immunopathogenesis of acute central nervous system disease produced by lymphocytic choriomeningitis virus. *J Exp Med* 135:874-889, 1972.

Wing EJ, Remington JS: Cell-mediated immunity and its role in resistance to infection. *West J Med* 126:14-31, 1977.

Viral Exanthems

Lawrence Corey, MD

Associate Professor of
Laboratory Medicine and Microbiology
University of Washington
and
Head, Virology Division
Children's Orthopedic Hospital and Medical Center
Seattle, WA 98105

Exanthems are cutaneous eruptions caused by systemic or contiguous spread of an organism, and some are characteristic of their etiologic agents. Classification and description of the type of exanthem can point to its etiology. Is it maculopapular, vesicular, or petechial? What is its distribution? How and at what season of the year did it evolve? What signs and symptoms are associated? The patient's epidemiologic characteristics also provide clues. How old is the patient? To what has he been exposed? To what has he been immunized? The etiology of an exanthem in an acutely ill, febrile patient can indicate appropriate treatment.

Some exanthems, such as Koplik's spots in patients with measles, occur only with a particular viral infection. In general, viral-induced maculopapular exanthems can be distinguished from maculopapular rashes associated with drug reactions, bacteria, mycoplasma, or rickettsial or immunologic reactions because the viral exanthems spare the palms and soles. The others may produce palmar or plantar exanthems. However, many viral-induced maculopapular exanthems are not specific enough to differentiate one virus infection from another.

Exanthems of infectious viral diseases may follow direct inoculation of the virus into the skin or indirect lymphogenous, hematogenous, or contiguous spread of the virus. Exanthems may result from virus multiplication in the skin or dermal vasculature or from the patient's immune response. They may occur in the epidermis or the vascular or extravascular structures of the dermis.

This chapter briefly reviews some of the more common viral exanthems.

VESICULAR ERUPTIONS

Herpes simplex virus (HSV) 1 or 2, varicella-zoster virus, the poxviruses, coxsackie A16 virus or other less frequently occurring coxsackieviruses (A4, A5, A9, and A10) cause most viral vesicular lesions. In rare instances, infections with enteroviruses or nonviral agents such as *Mycoplasma pneumoniae* have caused vesicular lesions.

Herpes simplex virus

Seroepidemiologic studies have shown that infections with herpes simplex virus are prevalent worldwide and that prevalence varies according to age, race, and socioeconomic status. Two antigenic types of herpes simplex virus exist: HSV-1 and HSV-2. In general HSV-1 infections occur predominantly above the diaphragm and HSV-2 infections below the diaphragm. However, these are only guidelines, and recent evidence suggests increasing frequency of genital HSV-1 infections. Through person-to-person contact, virus is generally inoculated onto susceptible mucous membrane directly or through a break in the skin. This transmission occurs when virus is excreted peripherally from an infected person.

Clinical manifestations of herpes simplex virus infections range from asymptomatic to severe and extensive infections, depending on whether the patient is experiencing the first episode of the disease or a recurrence (Figure 5.1). The incubation period is believed to be two to 14 days (mean: six to seven days). Characteristically, lesions start as vesicles, become pustular, break open, and coalesce into ulcers (Figure 5.2). The initial inflammatory response is polymorphonuclear with later lymphocytic infiltration. Herpetic lesions contain cells with eosinophilic intranuclear inclusions and multinucleated giant cells.

First, or primary, infection with either HSV-1 or HSV-2 usually causes multiple bilateral lesions at multiple anatomic sites. Viral shedding continues for an average of 12 days, and lesions persist for approximately three

Figure 5.1. Child with primary herpetic gingivostomatitis.

Figure 5.2. Ulcer resulting from the coalescence of herpes simplex lesions.

weeks. In patients with either primary symptomatic or asymptomatic infection, the virus may ascend peripheral nerves into dorsal and autonomic nerve root ganglia and become latent. Reactivation of latent virus from dorsal nerve root ganglia is thought to cause recurrence of the disease with reappearance of virus on the mucocutaneous surface.

Sequelae of HSV infections may include aseptic meningitis, autonomic nervous system dysfunction, or cutaneous infection at distant sites. Herpes simplex virus encephalitis usually occurs in patients who have had latent oral-labial disease (see chapter 6). Occasionally visceral dissemination to internal organs such as the liver, adrenals, or lung may lead to fulminant disease. Extensive HSV infections may recur in immunocompromised patients who have T-cell abnormalities, such as thymic dysplasia or Wiskott-Aldrich syndrome, or in patients who are receiving immunosuppressive therapy. One major complication of genital HSV is vertical transmission to the neonate with subsequent development of neonatal HSV (see chapter 8).

Antiviral chemotherapy can shorten the duration of viral shedding and ameliorate many of the symptoms of mucocutaneous HSV infections (see chapter 10). Topical antiviral agents have effectively alleviated herpetic keratitis.

Acyclovir has recently been approved for treatment of first episodes of genital herpes infection and limited, non-life-threatening, mucocutaneous HSV in immunocompromised patients. It does not eradicate latent infection and only slightly shortens the course of recurrent disease. Recurrences after acyclovir therapy are common.

Acute herpetic gingivostomatitis, a primary infection of the mucous membranes of the mouth, is the most common herpes infection of childhood and usually occurs between the ages of 1 and 4 years. Lesions in the anterior or posterior pharynx or both are generally

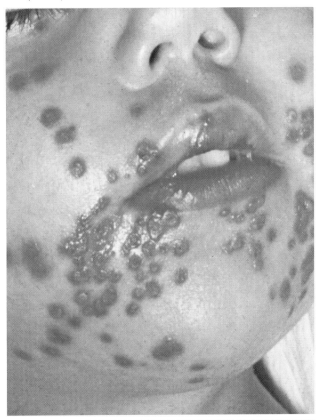

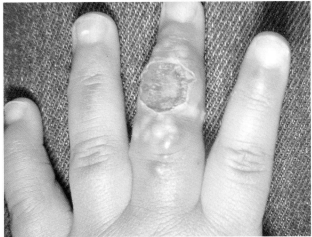

56

Figure 5.3. Multinucleated giant cells in the Papanicolaou smear from a woman with herpes simplex virus cervicitis.

Figure 5.4. Recurrent genital herpes simplex infection.

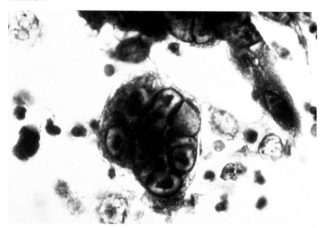

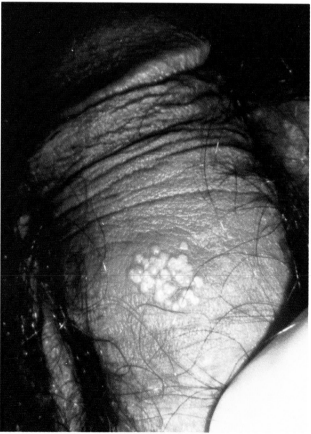

associated with cervical adenopathy, fever, headache, and malaise. The virus becomes latent in the trigeminal nerve root ganglia, and the disease recurs as classical unilateral fever blisters generally not associated with any systemic manifestations. The fever blisters last seven to ten days. About 50% to 70% of patients will perceive a slight tingling from hours to two days before a vesicle appears.

Genital herpes simplex infection is now one of the most common sexually transmitted diseases in the United States. Primary genital infection first causes pain, itching, dysuria, urethral discharge, or some combination of the four. These symptoms progress to severe, painful vulvovaginitis; balanitis; or urethritis. Characteristically, multiple, bilaterally distributed groups of umbilicated vesicles become pustular and coalesce into painful ulcers.

HSV cervicitis, a common manifestation of genital HSV infection, causes the release of multinucleated giant cells visible in the Papanicolaou smear (Figure 5.3). Systemic complaints such as fever, headache, malaise, and myalgias occur in about one third of the patients. Recurrent genital HSV infection is usually unilateral with fewer lesions and milder symptoms than the primary infection (Figure 5.4).

Herpetic whitlow, a recurrent infection of the fingers and hands, may be caused by either HSV-1 or HSV-2. Recurrent herpetic whitlow is often mistaken for bacterial cellulitis because of common characteristics: painful pustular lesions associated with streaking over the lymphatic vessels and axillary adenopathy. The disease is especially common in people in the medical and dental professions.

H simplex virus pharyngitis, a form of pharyngitis, is often misdiagnosed as streptococcal pharyngitis. HSV causes ulcerative lesions of the posterior pharynx, and the lesions are usually associated with fever, headache, and cervical lymphadenopathy. The infection is especially prevalent in college-aged people.

Herpetic keratoconjunctivitis causes symptoms ranging from mild conjunctivitis to characteristic superficial dendritic keratitis to deep stromal lesions, which can produce scarring and blindness. Pain, photophobia, and chemosis are the most common symptoms. The disease recurs in approximately 40% of patients. (See also chapter 9.)

Eczema herpeticum or Kaposi's varicelliform eruption is a widespread cutaneous infection in patients with preexisting skin diseases such as atopic eczema (Figure 5.5). Primary infection in children is usually extensive, but patients with chronic skin diseases may have mild, recurrent attacks.

Varicella-zoster virus

Herpesvirus varicella causes both varicella (chickenpox) and herpes zoster (shingles) infections, depending on the patient's age and other characteristics.

Varicella, a ubiquitous infection, occurs most commonly in 5- to 9-year-olds but rarely in adults. Its incubation period varies from 10 to 20 days, usually 14 to 16 days. Both droplets from the respiratory tracts of infected patients and direct contact with lesions can infect someone else. The infectious period is generally thought to last from the day before the rash appears until all vesicles have dried. Chickenpox is as highly contagious as measles and smallpox, and nosocomial infections have been reported. The incidence declines in the summer. Antibody may persist for life.

After a short prodrome with fever and headache or no prodrome, the typical pruritic rash appears. In the

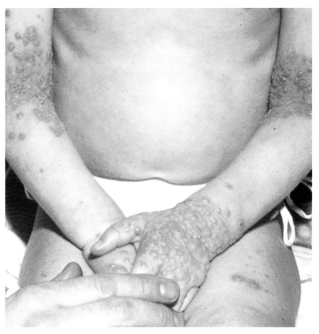

Figure 5.5. Eczema herpeticum, or Kaposi's varicelliform eruption, due to herpes simplex infection.

superficial layers of the skin, the thin, easily ruptured vesicle resembles a dewdrop on a rose petal (Figure 5.6). Lesions first appear in crops over the trunk, scalp, face, arms, and legs with the greatest concentration on the trunk (Figure 5.7). Successive crops appear for three days. Consequently, any one anatomic area has lesions in all stages: macules, papules, vesicles, and crusts. The number of vesicles may vary from a few scattered lesions to hundreds of lesions covering the entire skin surface of the body. Vesicles may also appear on mucous membranes, especially the palate. Biopsy of the lesions will show characteristic nuclear inclusions and giant cells like those with HSV infections.

In the immunocompetent young child, varicella is usually benign and does not require either hospitalization or antiviral chemotherapy. In 20% to 30% of immunosuppressed patients, hemorrhagic, progressive varicella may occur with pancreatitis, hepatitis, pneumonitis, and encephalitis. Mortality may reach 10%. In these patients antiviral treatment is warranted and appears to decrease visceral dissemination (see chapter 10). In immunocompromised children who have played with or live with patients with acute varicella, zoster immune globulin or zoster immune plasma given within three days of exposure either prevents or ameliorates varicella zoster infection. Staphylococcal or streptococcal bacterial superinfection or both occur in 3% to 10% of immunocompromised patients, and appropriate therapy should be administered.

Encephalitis occurs in less than one of every 1,000 patients with varicella. Differentiation of varicella encephalitis from Reye's syndrome after varicella may be difficult. The cerebrospinal fluid of patients with varicella encephalitis will yield lymphocytes, but the cerebrospinal fluid of patients with Reye's syndrome will be normal.

Congenital varicella syndrome is uncommon. It is usually associated with varicella in the mother in the first trimester or immediately postpartum. Severe or fatal varicella in the 5- to 10-day-old infant may occur if the mother has had varicella four days or less before delivery. These infants receive the virus but not antibody through the placenta. Often their disease disseminates. (See also chapter 8.)

Herpes zoster is chiefly a disease of adults. Its frequency increases in older people and immunocompromised patients, especially those with Hodgkin's disease or an organ transplant.

Patients with classic zoster infection usually experience severe pain and tenderness along the involved nerve root, and some of them have a fever. Lesions start as maculopapules, rapidly vesiculate, and coalesce into larger ulcers. The unilateral lesions do not cross the midline and appear most commonly on the shoulders, arms, neck, and lumbar-sacral region of the trunk. The lesions may last as long as three to four weeks. Virus can be isolated from lesions until they start to crust over.

Herpes zoster also infects the cranial nerves. Scleral and corneal lesions follow infection of the ophthalmic division of the trigeminal nerve. Pain, a vesicular eruption in the auditory canal, or facial paralysis may follow infection of the geniculate ganglia of the facial nerve.

In about 30% of adults older than 55, postherpetic neuralgia, a continued sharp pain in the area infected, lasts for months after the lesions heal. Viremia with dissemination and development of hepatitis, pneumonitis (Figure 5.8), and encephalitis may follow herpes zoster infection in patients with immune cellular abnormalities.

Intravenously administered vidarabine has decreased the duration of viral shedding and the time for scab formation and healing in immunocompromised patients. Its efficacy seems greater in younger adults than in older adults. In a recent study of intravenous acyclovir in elderly immunocompetent patients with varicella-zoster infection, lesions healed more quickly than in

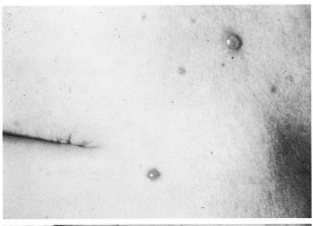

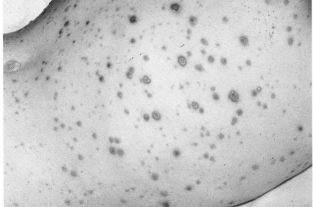

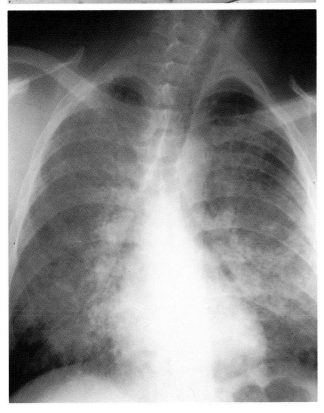

Figure 5.6. Varicella vesicle.

Figure 5.7. Varicella on the trunk of a child with leukemia.

Figure 5.8. Roentgenogram of diffuse interstitial pneumonia in an immunosuppressed patient with herpes zoster.

untreated patients. The drug's effect on postherpetic neuralgia needs further exploration.

The poxviruses

Modern medicine has eradicated *smallpox* from the world, and this is one major medical achievement in the 20th century. Poxvirus variola caused smallpox, an acute, highly contagious disease. It began with a three- to four-day prodrome of chills, fever, headache, backache, vomiting, and prostration. Vesicular eruption first appeared peripherally and then spread toward the trunk. In any one body region, lesions were at the same stage.

Vaccinia is an acute infectious disease caused by a laboratory poxvirus used to produce immunity to smallpox. With primary vaccination, the inoculated site progresses from reddened, to pruritic, to pustular, to papular, and to vesicular by the fifth to sixth day after inoculation. Then it progresses from pustular to crusted. By the end of the third week, the scab falls off and leaves a permanent scar that eventually becomes white. These signs may also be accompanied by fever and lymphadenopathy.

Vaccination of a partially immune person produces an attenuated and briefer form of vaccinia with no fever or regional lymphadenopathy. Revaccination of an adequately immunized person produces erythema and a papule but no vesiculation or constitutional symptoms. Autovaccinia follows scratching which accidentally transfers virus from the vaccination site to other areas (Figure 5.9), but no problems result unless other microbes also infect the site.

In patients with deficits in cell-mediated immunity, generalized vaccinia may occur (Figure 5.10). Similarly, in patients with eczema, *eczema vaccinatum* like that caused by herpes virus may occur (Figure 5.11). Postvaccinial encephalitis, serious but rare, occurs in approximately one of 100,000 people vaccinated. It usually causes fever, headache, vomiting, meningismus, paralysis, drowsiness, coma, and convulsions. It also causes

60

Figure 5.9. Autovaccinia.

Figure 5.10. Vaccinia.

Figure 5.11. Eczema vaccinatum lesions caused by vaccinia.

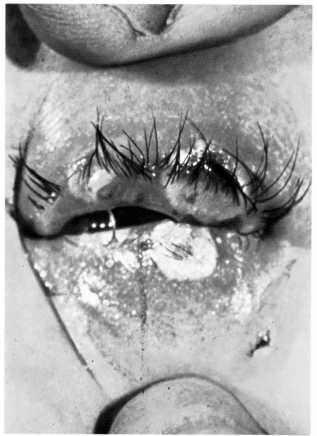

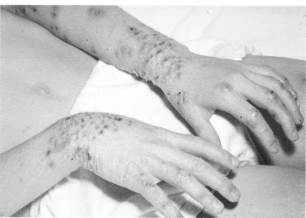

lymphocytosis in the cerebrospinal fluid, perivascular infiltration, and demyelination in the brain. Mortality may be as high as 30% to 40%. With the eradication of smallpox, routine vaccination is no longer recommended in the United States.

PAPULAR ERUPTIONS
Molluscum contagiosum

This is a benign epidermal lesion, a rounded, dome-shaped, waxy, pearly white papule with an umbilical central core (Figure 5.12). The core contains cheesy material that stains blue with Giemsa stain and is composed of molluscum bodies, each of which is a mass of viral particles (Figure 3.10d).

The lesions occur principally on the face, eyelids, trunk, and anogenital areas. These lesions usually last for six months to a year before resolving spontaneously. In occasional patients, the lesions persist and spread for three to four years. Eventually they regress spontaneously without scarring, and recurrences are rare. This poxvirus infection can be transmitted directly through sexual intercourse or, like other poxviruses, through fomites such as shared towels. The incubation period varies from two weeks to two months.

Table
Viral exanthems associated with coxsackie and other enteroviruses

Virus type		Age group	Occurrence of rash	Characteristic of rash	Associated manifestations
Coxsackievirus	A2	Children	Rare	Maculopapular	Fever
	A4	Children	Rare	Maculopapular, vesicular	Fever, herpangina, hepatitis
	A5	Mainly children	Occasional	Hand, foot, and mouth syndrome	Fever
	A7	Children and adults	Rare	Morbilliform; hand, foot, and mouth syndrome	Meningitis, pneumonia, pancarditis
	A9	Mainly children	4%	Maculopapular; vesicular; urticarial; petechial; hand, foot, and mouth syndrome	Fever, meningitis, pneumonia
	A10	Mainly children	Occasional	Hand, foot, and mouth syndrome	Fever
	A16	Children and adults	88%, <5 yr 38%, 5-12 yr 11%, adults	Hand, foot, and mouth syndrome	Fever
	B1	Children	Occasional	Maculopapular, vesicular	Fever, meningitis
	B2	Children	Rare	Maculopapular, vesicular, petechial	Fever, herpangina, meningitis
	B3	Mainly children	Occasional	Maculopapular, vesicular, petechial	Fever, hepatosplenomegaly
	B4	Mainly children	Occasional	Maculopapular, petechial, urticarial	Fever, respiratory
	B5	Mainly children	10%	Maculopapular, petechial, urticarial	Fever, meningitis
Echovirus	1	Children	Rare	Maculopapular	Conjunctivitis
	2	Children	Rare	Macular, maculopapular	Fever, pharyngitis
	3	Children	Rare	Petechial	Fever, meningitis
	4	Mainly children	10-20%	Macular, maculopapular, petechial	Fever, meningitis
	5	Infants and adults	Occasional	Macular	Fever
	6	Mainly children	Rare	Maculopapular, macular, papulopustular	Fever, meningitis
	7	Children	Occasional	Maculopapular	Fever
	9	Children and adults	57%, <5 yr 41%, 5-9 yr 6%, >10 yr	Maculopapular, petechial, vesicular	Fever, meningitis
	11	Mainly children	Occasional	Maculopapular, vesicular, urticarial	Fever, meningitis
	13	Children	Rare	Maculopapular	
	14	Mainly children	Rare	Maculopapular, scarlatiniform	Fever, meningitis
	16	Children	Occasional	Roseola-like	Fever, herpangina
	17	Children	Occasional	Macular, maculopapular, papulovesicular	Fever, diarrhea, herpangina, meningitis
	18	Children and adults	Occasional, 1 epidemic	Rubelliform	Fever, meningitis
	19	Children and adults	Occasional	Maculopapular	Fever, meningitis, upper respiratory
	22	Infants	Rare	Morbilliform	Respiratory
	25	Children	Occasional	Maculopapular, hemangioma-like	Fever, pharyngitis
	30	Children and adults	Occasional	Macular, maculopapular	Fever, meningitis
	32	Children	Rare	Hemangioma-like	Fever
	33	Not determined	Rare	Not determined	Meningitis, pyrexia
Enterovirus	71	Children	1 outbreak	Maculopapular; hand, foot, and mouth syndrome	Fever, meningitis

Figure 5.12. Molluscum contagiosum.

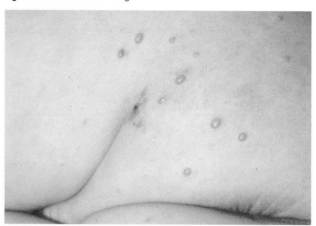

MACULOPAPULAR ERUPTIONS

Enteroviruses

This group of small RNA viruses consists of polioviruses, coxsackieviruses, and echoviruses, all of which infect the human alimentary tract. In humans the enteroviruses cause a variety of diseases ranging from minor febrile illness to paralysis (see Table). While subclinical illness is more common than obvious disease, enteroviruses also cause clinical diseases, especially in children. Rash, a common result of infection with many enteroviruses not in the polio group, is accompanied by various symptoms such as abdominal pain, upper respiratory symptoms, headache, malaise, and anorexia.

Diagnosis depends upon isolation and identification of the virus responsible or demonstration of a type-specific antibody reaction as discussed in chapter 3. Usually virus replicates in the gastrointestinal tract and can be recovered from the stool, urine, blood, and mucous membranes. The clinical course of infections depends upon several factors, including the strain of the virus and the host's susceptibility.

The portal of entry of enteroviruses is the alimentary tract via the mouth. The incubation period usually ranges from seven to 14 days but may range from two to 35 days. After the virus replicates in the gastrointestinal tract, the blood or lymph spreads the virus to various target tissues, including the spinal cord, brain, meninges, myocardium, pancreas, and skin. The virus replicates again at the secondary site to cause symptoms of the disease. Usually the virus is excreted in the feces and from the pharynx for one to four weeks after infection.

For the nonpolio viruses, no specific control measures are known. Young children should avoid contact with patients with acute febrile illness, especially those patients with a rash. During the enteroviral season, members of institutional staffs responsible for caring for infants should take the necessary precautions to avoid direct contact with susceptible infants.

Humans are the only known reservoirs of the enteroviruses, and close human contact is the primary avenue of spread. Fecal contamination of foods, utensils, and fingers are common sources of infections. Seasonal outbreaks are common during warm weather.

Measles

Measles is a distinct childhood disease, the most prominent signs of which are a macular exanthem and characteristic Koplik's spots (Figure 5.13). A safe, attenuated live virus vaccine is available and appears to impart long-lasting immunity. Before the introduction of measles vaccine in the United States, between 200,000 and 400,000 cases occurred annually. Since the vaccine was introduced, the number of reported cases has decreased more than 95%. In the United States a concentrated effort to eradicate measles is under way. To accomplish this goal, a large proportion of the population will have to be vaccinated because spontaneous outbreaks still occur in partially vaccinated populations. In industrialized countries, measles epidemics correspond closely with the school year; they peak in the late spring and diminish during the summer. Measles and secondary sequelae accounted for 1% of all deaths worldwide in a typical prevaccine year.

Figure 5.13. Koplik's spots.   63

The measles virus has no nonhuman reservoirs and no vectors. It is efficiently spread by aerosol into the respiratory tract. The most infectious stage of disease is associated with sneezing and coughing, which facilitate virus spread. An incubation period that usually lasts ten to 12 days follows infection. With the onset of the prodrome, virus is shed in the nasal secretions, throat, and urine. The patient has malaise, fever, copious coryza, cough, and conjunctivitis sometimes associated with photophobia. Koplik's spots appear on the oral membranes and mucosal surfaces at the end of the prodrome. With the appearance of the macular rash, neutralizing antibodies first become detectable in the serum and reach peak titers about 30 days later. Immunity following infection appears to be life-long.

Clinical diagnosis is reliable. Diagnosis by virus isolation is difficult, but serologic documentation of increased antibody titer is useful. The appearance of Koplik's spots is useful since they appear early and are unique. The prodrome is associated with higher fever and lasts longer than the rubella prodrome. No specific treatment exists.

Although measles is most often a self-limiting infection, more serious forms of the disease may occur. Measles encephalitis occurs in about one in 2,000 patients with measles and occurs two to three times more frequently in children over the age of ten than in children under the age of 5.

A high proportion of children who have had measles encephalitis are left with neurologic sequelae. *Subacute sclerosing panencephalitis* (SSPE) is a rare, slow neurologic disease of older children. It is accompanied by high antimeasles antibody titers in the serum and cerebrospinal fluid. Children with SSPE usually live six to 12 months. The pathogenesis of SSPE is not completely understood. Some evidence suggests that an abnormal host-immune response or a variant measles virus or both are involved. Measles vaccination appears to have decreased the incidence of SSPE.

Otitis media is the most common complication of measles, and bacterial infections of the upper respiratory tract are the second most common.

Rubella

Rubella (German measles) is characterized by mild symptoms and generalized rash. Before the introduction of vaccine, rubella epidemics occurred every six to nine years with the highest incidences in March, April, and May. The incidence peaks in five- to nine-year-olds. Rubella infections rarely occur in preschool children, but many cases have been reported in adolescents and young adults.

The infection is transmitted through close person-to-person contact. The virus is excreted in the oropharyngeal secretions and spread by the respiratory tract. The virus is communicable for five to seven days before and three to five days after clinical signs appear. Infants with congenital infections shed large quantities of virus, and it can persist in their throats for many months.

Subclinical infections occur as often as clinical infections. The incubation period ranges from 12 to 21 days. Usually nontender lymphadenopathy precedes the appearance of a macular rash that begins on the face and spreads downward rapidly. The rash turns to a reddish blush and disappears after three or four days. The constitutional symptoms are more severe in adults who suffer from arthralgia or arthritis or both. Clinical diagnosis requires laboratory confirmation. No specific treatment for rubella exists.

The serious complications are congenital abnormalities, fetal deaths, and spontaneous abortions of mothers with infants infected in utero. Fetal infection during the first trimester appears to be the most critical; it produces anomalies in 50% of fetuses. The major anomalies are cardiovascular or ocular lesions, microcephaly, mental retardation, and general growth retardation. (See also chapter 8.)

Selected References

Bean B, Braun C, Balfour HH: Acyclovir therapy for acute herpes zoster. *Lancet* 2:118-121, 1982.

Cherry JD: Non-polio enteroviruses, in Feigin RD, Cherry JD (eds): *Textbook of Pediatric Infectious Disease.* Philadelphia, WB Saunders Co, 1981.

Boyden SV (ed): *The Impact of Civilization on the Biology of Man.* Toronto, Univ of Toronto Press, 1970.

Gilchrest B, Barden HP: Photodistribution of viral exanthema. *Pediatrics* 54:136-138, 1974.

Krugman S, Ward R, Katz SL: *Infectious Diseases in Children,* ed 6. St Louis, The CV Mosby Co. 1977.

Lerner AM, Klein JO, Cherry JD: New viral exanthems. *N Engl J Med* 269: 678-685, 1963.

Peterslund NA, Seyer-Hansen K, Ipsen J, et al: Acyclovir in herpes zoster. *Lancet* 2:827-830, 1981.

Wenner HA: Virus diseases associated with cutaneous eruptions. *Prog Med Virol* 16:269-336, 1973.

Viral Respiratory Diseases

Robert B. Couch, MD

Professor, Departments of Microbiology
and Immunology, and Medicine
Director, Influenza Research Center
Baylor College of Medicine
Houston, TX 77030

More than 200 distinct viruses can infect the human respiratory tract. They constitute a diverse group with respect to size, symmetry, nucleic-acid type, lability, and replication strategy. Each virus can produce a variety of respiratory disease syndromes, and each syndrome may be caused by a variety of respiratory viruses. The major viruses are shown in Table 6.1. Among the diseases caused by respiratory viruses are the common cold, the most common illness in humans, and influenza, perhaps the last of the pandemic diseases. The severity of viral respiratory disease ranges from inapparent infection to overwhelming infection and disease, which may be fatal. It is difficult to overestimate the impact these viruses have on human health.

Annually in the United States, more than half of all acute illnesses are respiratory. A one-year distribution by age, sex, and syndrome is shown in Table 6.2. A number of viruses responsible for other disease syndromes may also produce acute respiratory symptoms. Such viruses or viral diseases include measles (rubeola), mumps, three-day measles (rubella), chickenpox (varicella), lymphocytic choriomeningitis virus, and cytomegalovirus. The incidence of acute respiratory illnesses is similar in all geographic areas of the United States. The incidence in the winter is about twice that in the summer; and in fall and spring, the incidence is between the other two rates. In tropical climates, the incidence is greatest during the rainy season.

ACUTE RESPIRATORY DISEASES

Respiratory diseases are usually designated as upper respiratory or lower respiratory (Table 6.3), and various symptoms may be present (Figure 6.1). Most illnesses are acute, relatively mild, and self-limited, but more severe illness commonly occurs in infants infected with one of several viruses and in elderly or chronically ill persons infected with influenza virus. The most common complications are secondary bacterial infections that cause otitis media, sinusitis, or pneumonia.

Figure 6.1. Syndromes and symptoms of upper and lower viral respiratory diseases.

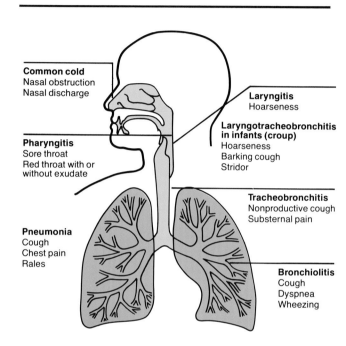

A specific viral respiratory disease syndrome can frequently be diagnosed by considering the symptoms, patient's age, time of year, population involved, and pattern of illnesses in the community. Definitive viral diagnosis requires isolation of the causative virus or demonstration of a rise in antibody titer.

MAJOR RESPIRATORY VIRUSES
Influenza viruses

Influenza viruses (for an example, see Figure 6.2) constitute the only genus of the Orthomyxoviridae family. There are three subtypes of human type A viruses and numerous antigenic variants of types A and B. Such variation has not been described for type C.

Antigenic variants result from *antigenic shift* (major antigenic variation) or *antigenic drift* (minor antigenic variation). Antigenic shift has occurred if antisera to one or both of the surface antigens (hemagglutinin and neuraminidase) of recently prevalent strains exhibit *no* cross-

Table 6.1.
Viruses that cause respiratory disease in humans

	Serotypes		Serotypes commonly producing respiratory disease in…		
	Number	Number causing respiratory illness	Infants <2 yr	Children 2-18 yr	Adults >18 yr
Adenoviridae	39	9	1, 2, 3, 5, 7	1, 2, 3, 5, 7	3, 4, 7, 14, 21*
Coronaviridae	3	3	—	229E, OC43, B814	229E, OC43, B814
Herpesviridae					
Herpes simplex virus	2	1	1	1	1
Epstein-Barr virus	1	1	—	1	1
Orthomyxoviridae					
Influenza viruses	3	3	A, B	A, B	A, B
Paramyxoviridae					
Parainfluenza viruses	4	4	1, 2, 3	1, 2, 3	—
Respiratory syncytial virus	1	1	1	1	—
Picornaviridae					
Enteroviruses	72	19	—	Cox A2, 4, 5, 6, 8, 10	Cox A21*
Rhinoviruses	>110	>110	All	All	All

*The incidence of adenovirus types 4, 7, 14, and 21 and coxsackievirus A21 may be particularly high in military populations.

Table 6.2.
Incidence of acute respiratory conditions per 100 persons per year in the United States (1978-1979)

		Acute upper respiratory		Influenza		Other acute respiratory conditions		
	General incidence	Common cold	Other upper respiratory	With digestive manifestations	Other influenza	Pneumonia	Bronchitis	All other acute respiratory
Both sexes								
All ages	116.9	45.9	15.1	2.7	46.5	1.5	2.9	2.3
Males								
All ages	109.1	43.3	14.2	2.4	42.6	1.5	2.8	2.24
Females								
All ages	124.2	48.4	15.9	3.0	50.1	1.5	3.0	2.2
Both sexes								
<6	203.0	130.3		56.1			16.6	
6-16	158.9	90.2		61.3			7.5	
17-44	117.3	56.6		55.4			5.3	
≥45	66.3	29.4		31.6			5.3	
Males								
<6	200.0	126.1		55.6			18.3	
6-16	148.8	83.7		56.7			8.4	
17-44	104.5	50.5		49.6			4.4	
≥45	59.4	27.6		27.1			4.7	
Females								
<6	206.1	134.7		56.7			14.7	
6-16	169.5	97.0		65.9			6.5	
17-44	129.2	62.3		60.9			6.0	
≥45	71.9	30.9		35.3			5.7	

Table 6.3.
Viral respiratory diseases

	Predominant symptoms	Most common viral causes in...		
		Infants	Children	Adults
Upper respiratory				
Common cold	Nasal obstruction Nasal discharge	Rhinoviruses Adenoviruses Influenza viruses Parainfluenza viruses Respiratory syncytial virus	Rhinoviruses Adenoviruses Coronavirus Influenza viruses Parainfluenza viruses Respiratory syncytial virus	Rhinoviruses Coronavirus Influenza viruses Parainfluenza viruses Respiratory syncytial virus
Pharyngitis	Sore throat	Adenoviruses Coxsackieviruses Herpes simplex virus	Adenoviruses Coxsackieviruses	Adenoviruses Coxsackieviruses Herpes simplex virus
Lower respiratory				
Laryngitis/croup	Hoarseness "Barking" cough in infants	Parainfluenza viruses Influenza viruses	Parainfluenza viruses Influenza viruses	Parainfluenza viruses Influenza viruses
Tracheobronchitis	Cough	Parainfluenza viruses Influenza viruses	Parainfluenza viruses Influenza viruses	Influenza viruses Adenoviruses
Bronchiolitis	Cough Dyspnea	Respiratory syncytial virus Parainfluenza viruses	Rare	Rare
Pneumonia	Cough Chest pain	Respiratory syncytial virus Influenza viruses Parainfluenza viruses Adenoviruses	Influenza viruses Parainfluenza viruses Adenoviruses	Influenza viruses Adenoviruses

Table 6.4.
Human influenza viruses

Type	Subtype	Years of prevalence	Representative variants
A*	H1N1†	1918-1957‡	A/Puerto Rico/8/34 A/FM/1/47
	H2N2	1957-1967	A/Japan/305/57
	H3N2	1968-	A/Hong Kong/1/68 A/Victoria/3/75 A/Texas/1/77 A/Bangkok/1/79
	H1N1	1977-	A/USSR/92/77 A/England/333/80
B	None defined	1940- §	B/Hong Kong/5/72 B/Singapore/222/79
C	None defined	1949- ¶	C/JHB/2/66

*Type A viruses are also prevalent among pigs, horses, and birds.

†Earlier classifications of this subtype included separate designations for Hsw1N1, H0N1, and H1N1. All are now designated as the H1N1 subtype.

‡An influenza virus was first isolated from swine in 1931 and from man in 1933; retrospective serologic studies indicated that a swine/31-like virus became prevalent in humans in 1918.

§First isolated from humans in 1940.

¶First isolated from humans in 1949.

Figure 6.2. Electron micrograph of an influenza virus.

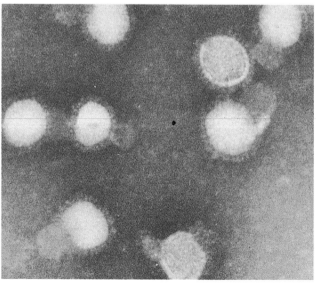

reactivity with newly isolated strains of the same type, and vice versa. Antigenic shift has been demonstrated only in type A influenza viruses; major changes have been identified only three times in the hemagglutinin antigen and twice in the neuraminidase antigen. The resulting antigens are designated H1, H2, H3, N1, and N2 (Table 6.4).

Antigenic drift has occurred if antisera to one or both of the surface antigens of recently prevalent strains exhibit reduced cross-reactivity with newly isolated strains of the same type, and vice versa. The newly isolated strains are then considered to be new variants. One of these new strains then serves as the prototype virus (representative variant) and is designated by type, location of first isolation, specimen number, and year of isolation (Table 6.4). Variants show definite but reduced crossreactivity with other variants of the same subtype. Antigenic drift occurs in all three types of influenza virus but is very minor with type C.

Influenza viruses are responsible for pandemic (worldwide), epidemic, and endemic occurrences of acute respiratory disease. A pandemic generally follows an antigenic shift and, thus, is limited to type A influenza viruses. Essentially all persons are susceptible, and large portions of various populations are affected by this widespread disease. In recent history, pandemics have occurred in 1889, 1918, 1957, and 1968.

Antigenic drift, on the other hand, leads to renewed susceptibility of a portion of the population. When the portion is sufficiently large, an epidemic of some degree will ensue. This tends to occur every one to three years for type A influenza and every three to six years for type B, even though the different influenza viruses are present every winter in temperate climates. Conditions most favorable for spread of influenza are (1) presence of infected and ill persons in an enclosed area (eg, classroom, institution), (2) a high proportion of susceptible persons crowded together, (3) low humidity, and (4) poor ventilation. Under such circumstances, infection rates may reach 60% to 80%.

A community epidemic of influenza, which begins in school-aged children, generally lasts four to six weeks. During the later stages, preschool children and adults predominate among the ill. Although influenza A and B epidemics predominate in school-aged children, influenza A infects a large proportion of all age groups.

Influenza viruses are transmitted primarily in air. Virus is initially deposited on the mucous covering of the tracheobronchial tree. The virus binds to neuraminic acid in the mucoprotein, but the action of neuraminidase induces release; the resulting liquefaction of mucus may promote access of virus to the mucosal surface. The incubation period is one to five days; during this interval, virus shedding progressively increases. The primary site of infection is the superficial columnar epithelium. Completion of a replicative cycle in these cells results in cellular death and desquamation; resulting edema and mononuclear infiltrations account for the local symptoms.

A patient who has typical influenza experiences sudden onset of fever, headache, myalgias, and lassitude; nonproductive cough, sore throat, and nasal symptoms also appear (Figure 6.3). The systemic symptoms usually last two to four days, but respiratory symptoms may persist for several days. Viremia has been reported but is rare; thus, an explanation for the prominent systemic symptoms is not currently available. Although typical influenza is described here, most patients either exhibit one of the syndromes listed in Table 6.3 or experience clinically inapparent infection.

A direct relationship exists between the quantity of virus detectable in secretions and the severity of illness. A decrease in the quantity of virus is accompanied by clinical improvement; this generally occurs before antibody is detectable. A role for interferon and cell-mediated immune mechanisms in recovery is suggested by results

Figure 6.3. Course of acute influenza infection, caused by type A H1N1 virus, in an otherwise healthy college student.

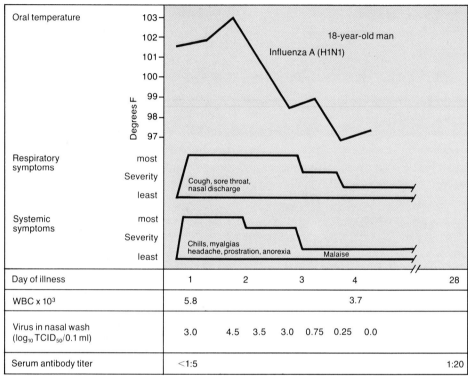

of in vitro and animal studies; however, antibody is the primary defense against acquisition of infection. Both serum IgG and secretory IgA antibodies are involved in this protection. Although the popular notion is that IgA is the mediator, proof for this is lacking. Regardless of which antibody is involved, antibody to the hemagglutinin is required since the role for antineuraminidase antibody is limited to impairing virus release.

Influenza may be specifically diagnosed by testing specimens of nasal or pharyngeal secretions in appropriate tissue cultures or embryonated hens' eggs. Rapid methods for viral diagnosis are being used increasingly. Diagnosis by antibody tests requires testing of sera from acutely ill and convalescent patients. Complement fixation or hemagglutination inhibition tests are usually used.

A number of complications have been clearly attrib-

uted to influenza (Table 6.5). The most significant is pneumonia, which is responsible for most deaths attributable to influenza (Figure 6.4). At greatest risk of death are infants and persons with chronic diseases, particularly heart or lung disease.

In the United States, inactivated influenza-virus vaccines containing current type A and B strains of virus are recommended annually for persons at risk of secondary pneumonia and death as a result of influenza. They include patients who have chronic cardiovascular disease, lung disease, neuromuscular disease, renal disease, cancer, or diabetes.

Vaccine prepared from virus grown in embryonated hens' eggs is formulated according to annual recommendations by the immunization advisory committees of the World Health Organization and the United States

Centers for Disease Control. Because of cocirculation of H3N2 and H1N1 viruses, recent formulations have included two type A viruses. The vaccine produces mild local and systemic reactions in a small proportion of patients.

During the 1976 national immunization program for swine influenza, the occurrence of Guillain-Barré syndrome increased in the eight-week period after vaccination; however, monitoring in subsequent years has not shown a relationship between vaccination and occurrence of the syndrome. Protection among persons given influenza virus vaccine usually varies between 50% and 90%, depending on the potency of the vaccine, extent of influenza activity, and antigenic relationship between the vaccine and epidemic viruses.

Amantadine, a chemotherapeutic agent that is effective for the prevention and treatment of type A influenza but ineffective for types B and C, may be used as an alternative to vaccine for type A influenza. Amantadine will prevent illness in 70% of people who receive it.

Respiratory syncytial virus and parainfluenza viruses
Respiratory syncytial virus (RSV) and parainfluenza viruses are members of the Paramyxoviridae family, which also includes the well-known mumps and measles viruses. Mumps virus is closely related to the parainfluenza viruses (genus *Paramyxovirus*), but measles virus and RSV (Figure 6.5) have distinguishing properties and occupy separate genuses, *Morbillivirus* and *Pneumovirus*, respectively. There are four parainfluenza virus serotypes but only one RSV serotype.

Members of the Paramyxoviridae family have no common antigen. Distinctive surface antigens describe four serotypes of parainfluenza viruses, mumps virus, and Newcastle virus, but some antigenic determinants are similar, so serologic crossreactions occur and may prevent specific serologic diagnosis. RSV antigens are distinctive; minor variations that have been de-

Table 6.5.
Complications of influenza

- **Pneumonia,** the most significant complication and responsible for most deaths attributable to influenza

  Influenzal
  Mixed influenzal-bacterial
  Secondary bacterial
- **Sinusitis** in patients of any age
- **Otitis media,** particularly in infants and small children
- **Reye's syndrome,** an acute toxic illness that occurs two to five days after apparent recovery from influenza. Patients exhibit encephalopathy and hepatomegaly resulting from acute fatty infiltration and encephalopathy. Either encephalopathy or hepatomegaly may lead to coma and death. The syndrome's pathogenesis is unknown.
- **Encephalitis,** rare but well documented
- **Acute myositis** may occur in children with influenza B infection.

Figure 6.4. Pneumonia and influenza mortality by age in certain epidemic years. Note the unique age distribution for 1918.

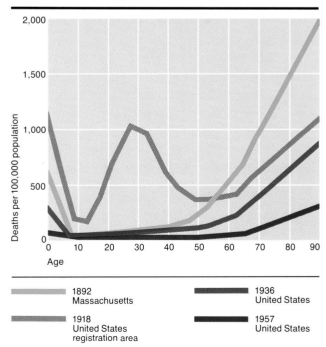

72

Figure 6.5. Syncytia caused by growth of respiratory syncytial virus in tissue culture of an epidermoid carcinoma (HEp-2). Note extensive fusing of cell membranes to produce multinucleated cells.

Figure 6.6. Patterns of occurrence of parainfluenza, respiratory syncytial, and influenza virus illnesses in Houston, Texas.

Figure 6.7. Chest x-ray films of 3-month-old infant with bronchiolitis caused by respiratory syncytial virus. Note the flattened diaphragm and increased lucency resulting from trapped air.

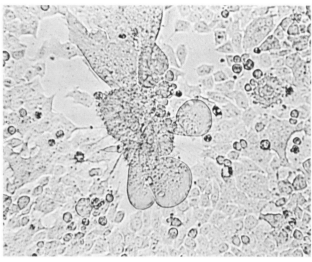

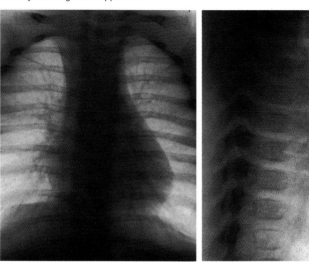

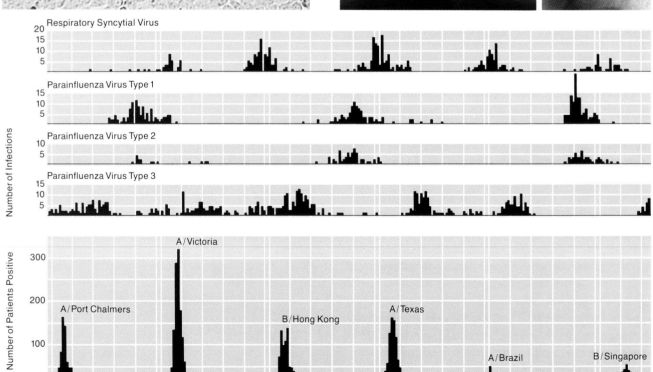

scribed are insufficient for serotype designations.

Parainfluenza viruses and RSV are common causes of acute respiratory disease throughout the world. Together with the influenza viruses, they constitute the most important cause of serious lower respiratory disease among infants and children. In temperate climates, parainfluenza viruses have been both epidemic and endemic; RSV has been only epidemic (Figure 6.6).

Up to 100% of 2-year-olds have been infected by RSV and 60% by parainfluenza virus type 3 (para 3). Reinfection with RSV and the parainfluenza viruses is common although illness with RSV is generally less severe. (See also chapter 8.)

RSV and the parainfluenza viruses will spread by contact with respiratory secretions; whether small-particle aerosols also transmit infection is unknown.

Because these viruses are highly infectious, a small inoculum dose probably suffices to initiate infection, and incubation periods appear to be two to eight days. Infection involves the superficial columnar epithelium, and edema and lymphocytic infiltrates account for local symptoms. Resulting impingement on the small lumen of the infant's airways accounts for the stridor of croup and the wheezing and hyperinflation of bronchiolitis.

Severe disease with parainfluenza virus and RSV infection occurs only in infants and small children. Para 1 is the most common cause of croup, para 2 may also cause croup, RSV is the most common cause of bronchiolitis, para 3 causes lower respiratory disease in infants, and para 4 causes mild upper respiratory illness only. Although the viruses may produce upper and lower respiratory illnesses (Table 6.3), infection may also be asymptomatic.

Croup, or acute laryngotracheobronchitis, is characterized by hoarseness; a characteristic barking, metallic cough; and noisy inspirations (inspiratory stridor). Upper respiratory signs and symptoms are also usually present. The symptoms, which tend to be worse at night, may frighten both child and parents. The syndrome must be differentiated from acute epiglottitis caused by *Hemophilus influenzae*, which responds to antibiotic therapy.

Bronchiolitis is characterized by dry, troublesome cough, dyspnea, rapid respirations, hyperresonant lungs, wheezing, and sometimes cyanosis. Infants with bronchiolitis (Figure 6.7) exhibit expiratory stridor similar to that of asthma rather than the inspiratory stridor of croup. Viral pneumonia may also be present, and it may be the primary symptom. In such cases, wheezing is minimal or absent, and clinical or x-ray findings suggest pneumonia.

Antigen-antibody complexes from maternal antibody, a cell-mediated immune reaction, and IgE-mediated bronchospasm have each been suggested as an immunopathologic basis for bronchiolitis and perhaps pneumonia with RSV; however, definitive evidence is lacking. The recovery process probably involves interferon, cell-mediated immune functions, and antibody. Resistance is mediated by antibody, and secretory IgA may play a primary role.

Specific diagnosis of RSV or parainfluenza virus infection requires virus isolation or demonstration of a specific antibody response. The best specimens for virus isolation are nasal or tracheal aspirates. A rise in the titer of antibody to RSV or parainfluenza virus may be demonstrated in complement fixation or neutralization tests; hemagglutination inhibition may also be used for parainfluenza viruses. Since the parainfluenza virus surface antigens share antigenic determinants, a specific serotype diagnosis by serology is not possible. Newer serologic methods such as ELISA (enzyme-linked immunosorbent assay) appear to be promising.

A complication of RSV and parainfluenza virus infections is acute respiratory insufficiency, which may lead to death, particularly in the patient who has underlying cardiopulmonary disease. Although other complications have been reported, causation is uncertain.

Treatment of RSV or parainfluenza viral infection is limited to symptomatic and physiologic supportive therapy. Vaccines are being developed. Recent reports suggest that breast-feeding may provide some prophylaxis.

Rhinoviruses

Rhinoviruses appear to exhibit a form of antigenic variation. Over 110 serotypes are detectable with immune animal sera, whereas the heterotypic antibody responses seen with hyperimmune animal sera and human sera indicate many shared antigenic determinants (as in antigenic drift of influenza viruses). In addition, the proportion of natural isolates with higher serotype numbers (more recent isolates) and untypable isolates increases with time (Table 6.6), again suggesting that antigenic drift occurs. Finally, antigenic variation of a serotype has been demonstrated in the laboratory.

Rhinoviruses are prevalent throughout the world. In temperate climates, they are prevalent in the fall in association with school openings and in spring for unknown reasons. In tropical areas, they predominate during the rainy season. In any geographic area, several rhinovirus serotypes will be causing colds, and the serotypes will be replaced slowly by other serotypes. All ages are involved, and infection rates range from 1.2 per person per year in infants to 0.7 in young adults to less than 0.5 in older persons.

Rhinoviruses spread easily in families, schools, military populations, and other institutionalized groups. In groups with close contact, infection rates may be as high as 80% to 90% during only a few weeks. In the home, the virus is usually introduced by a school-aged child. Risk of infection to other family members is great if the child's cold is severe, if his contact with other family members is prolonged, and if the family includes other young children.

Rhinoviruses are transmitted by direct or indirect contact, and they are highly communicable. Incubation periods are one to four days. Virus is detectable in nasal secretions near the onset of illness, and the severity of illness is directly related to the extent of mucosal involvement demonstrable in nasal scrapings and the quantity of virus in secretions. Direct cellular damage from infection accounts for the local edema, inflammation, and nasal discharge. Although lower respiratory illnesses have been reported in infants, small children, and some adults, they have not been severe, perhaps because rhinoviruses do not grow well at 37°C.

Rhinovirus common colds are characterized by prominent sneezing, nasal obstruction and discharge, and headache. A variety of other symptoms including malaise, myalgias, sore throat, hoarseness, and cough may also be present, but these symptoms are usually mild (Figure 6.8).

Mechanisms for recovery are unknown, but both interferon and antibody may be involved. Resistance is attributable to antibody, and evidence favors secretory IgA antibody as the primary mediator. Reinfection with the same serotype occurs but is uncommon.

Complications of rhinovirus illness include sinusitis and otitis media. Acute respiratory insufficiency in patients who have emphysema and asthmatic attacks in patients who have bronchial asthma may also occur.

Therapy is directed toward relief of distressing symptoms. Since no antiviral therapy or vaccines are available, preventive measures are limited to handwashing, good personal hygiene, and avoidance of finger to eye or nose contact.

Adenoviruses

Adenoviruses, common causes of infection, are less important causes of respiratory disease than other viruses. They cause about 5% of illnesses in infants and about 3% in young children. The infections occur among young civilian adults, but before a vaccine was available, epidemics of acute respiratory disease were fre-

Figure 6.8. Course of rhinovirus common cold in an otherwise healthy volunteer who was inoculated with nasal drops containing 10 $TCID_{50}$ of rhinovirus type 13.

									18-year-old man Rhinovirus type 13
Headache				+	+	+			
Cough				+	+	+			
Sore throat			+	+	+				
Nasal discharge				+++	++	++	+		
Nasal obstruction				+++	++	+			
Day after inoculation (10 $TCID_{50}$ by nasal drops)	0	1	2	3	4	5	6	7	28
Isolation of virus	0	0	+	+	+	+	0	0	
Serum antibody titer	<1:2								1:32

Table 6.6.
Distribution of rhinovirus serotypes in three studies

			Percentage of isolates		
	Years	Number of isolates	Types 1-55	Types 56-89	Untyped
Virginia	1963-1967 1968-1969	337 80	79 49	14 24	7 27
New York	1963-1965	168	80	20	2
Seattle	1966-1967 1968-1969	262 195	63 47	34 46	3 8
Tecumseh	1966-1967 1968-1969 1970-1971	83 130 58	71 42 40	22 42 10	7 16 50

quent in military recruits.

Effects of adenovirus on cells include lysis, induction of latent or chronic infection, and oncogenesis. Some childhood serotypes (1, 2, 5, and 6) appear likely to become latent; indeed, adenoviruses were discovered when spontaneous degeneration of cultures of adenoid tissue occurred. These serotypes may shed intermittently for years.

Adenoviruses are prevalent in children in late winter, spring, and early summer, and in military recruits in winter. Types 1, 2, 3, 5, and 7 predominate in children and types 4 and 7 in recruits. Adenoviruses exhibit a high degree of affinity for the intestinal tract; at least half of human infections are asymptomatic and may be detected only by fecal shedding. The fecal-oral route is the major mechanism for spread of adenoviruses.

Adenovirus infection is usually accompanied by upper respiratory disorders with prominent pharyngitis, but lower respiratory diseases, including pneumonia, are not uncommon among infants, children, and young adults. Pharyngoconjunctival fever is a distinct syndrome with prominent conjunctivitis and pharyngitis; it is most often caused by type 3 virus, which may be acquired in contaminated swimming pools.

No specific treatment is available for adenovirus, but a vaccine for types 4 and 7 has been highly effective in military recruits. The vaccine consists of live adenovirus incorporated into an enteric-coated capsule that bypasses the respiratory tract and induces an asymptomatic intestinal infection. The resulting immunity protects against respiratory infection.

Coronaviruses
Members of the coronavirus group cause a broad spectrum of diseases in a variety of animals including humans. The biology and epidemiology of these viruses are incompletely characterized; at least three serotypes have been identified, and they may cause infection in persons of all ages. Most prominent in winter, they cause about 15% of common colds in adults; however, they do not appear to be significant causes of lower respiratory disease. No specific treatment or preventive measure is available.

Selected
References

Baum SG: Adenovirus, in Mandell GL, Douglas RG, Bennett JE (eds): *Principles and Practice of Infectious Diseases.* New York, John Wiley & Sons, 1979, pp 1353-1361.

Chanock, RM: Parainfluenza viruses, in Lennette EH, Schmidt NJ (eds): *Diagnostic Procedures for Viral and Rickettsial Infections,* ed 5. Washington, DC, American Public Health Association, 1979, pp 611-632.

Chanock RM, Bell JA, Parrott RH: Natural history of parainfluenza infection, in Pollard M (ed): *Perspectives in Virology.* Minneapolis, Burgess Publishing Co, 1960, vol 2, pp 126-139.

Chanock RM, Hyun WK, Brandt C, et al: Respiratory syncytial virus, in Evans AS (ed): *Viral Infections of Humans: Epidemiology and Control.* New York, Plenum Publishing Corp, 1976, pp 365-382.

Couch RB, Kasel JA, Six HR, et al: The basis for immunity to influenza in man, in Nayak D, Fox CF (eds): *Genetic Variation Among Influenza Viruses.* New York, Academic Press Inc, 1981, vol 22, pp 535-546.

Data from the National Health Survey. Acute Conditions. Incidence and Associated Disability, United States, July 1977-June 1978, publication (PHS) 79-1560. US Dept of Health, Education, and Welfare, 1979, p 3.

Douglas RG, Betts RF: Influenza virus, in Mandell GL, Douglas RG, Bennett JE (eds): *Principles and Practice of Infectious Diseases.* New York, John Wiley & Sons, 1979, pp 1135-1167.

Fox JP: Is a rhinovirus vaccine possible? *Am J Epidemiol* 103:345-354, 1976.

Foy HM, Grayston JT: Adenoviruses, in Evans AS (ed): *Viral Infections of Humans: Epidemiology and Control.* New York, Plenum Publishing Corp, 1976, pp 53-69.

Glezen WP, Couch RB: Interpandemic influenza in the Houston area, 1974-76. *N Engl J Med* 298:587-592, 1978.

Glezen WP, Denny FW: Epidemiology of acute lower respiratory disease in children. *N Engl J Med* 288:498-505, 1973.

Glezen WP, Loda FA, Denny FW: The parainfluenza viruses, in Evans AS (ed): *Viral Infections of Humans: Epidemiology and Control.* New York, Plenum Publishing Corp, 1976, pp 337-349.

Gwaltney JM Jr: Medical reviews: Rhinoviruses. *Yale J Biol Med* 48:17-45, 1975.

Hall CB: Respiratory syncytial virus, in Mandell GL, Douglas RG, Bennett JE (eds): *Principles and Practice of Infectious Diseases.* New York, John Wiley & Sons, 1979, pp 1186-1203.

Kasel JA: Adenoviruses, in Lennette EH, Schmidt NJ (eds): *Diagnostic Procedures for Viral, Rickettsial, and Chlamydial Infections.* Washington, DC, American Public Health Association, 1979, pp 229-255.

Kilbourne ED: *The Influenza Viruses and Influenza.* New York, Academic Press Inc, 1975.

McIntosh K: Coronavirus, in Mandell GL, Douglas RG, Bennett JE (eds): *Principles and Practice of Infectious Diseases.* New York, John Wiley & Sons, 1979, pp 1212-1217.

Monto AS: Coronaviruses, in Evans AS (ed): *Viral Infections of Humans: Epidemiology and Control.* New York, Plenum Publishing Corp, 1976, pp 127-141.

Schonberger LB, Bregman DJ, Sullivan-Bolyai JZ, et al: Guillain-Barré syndrome following vaccination in the National Influenza Immunization Program, United States, 1976-1977. *Am J Epidemiol* 110:105-123, 1979.

Stuart-Harris CH, Schild GC: *Influenza: The Viruses and the Disease.* Littleton, Mass, Publishing Sciences Group Inc, 1976.

Viral Infections of the Nervous System

James F. Bale, Jr, MD
Assistant Professor
Division of Pediatric Neurology
Department of Pediatrics
University of Iowa College of Medicine
Iowa City, IA 52242

Earl R. Kern, PhD
Research Associate Professor
Division of Infectious Disease
Department of Pediatrics
University of Utah School of Medicine
Salt Lake City, UT 84132

HISTORICAL OVERVIEW

The concept that viruses can infect and damage the central nervous system (CNS) evolved in the 20th century. Although scientists of the 1800s recognized that disorders such as rabies and poliomyelitis might be caused by infectious agents, the nature of the agents and the pathogenesis of these illnesses were poorly understood. An important breakthrough occurred in 1909, when Landsteiner and Popper demonstrated that the agent responsible for poliomyelitis was filterable and, thus, was not a bacterium and that this disease could be transmitted from humans to monkeys. In the same decade, similar experiments indicated that rabies has a viral origin.

Despite these initial successes, knowledge of viral CNS disorders accumulated slowly. Because viruses require living cells for growth, cell culture methods had to be developed and perfected. Once this was accomplished, research in neurovirology expanded rapidly. In the 1930s, a laboratory strain of poliovirus was successfully grown in human embryonic nerve tissue; but the most important advance came in 1948, when Enders, Robbins, and Weller reported that wild-type polioviruses could be grown in nonneural human embryonic tissue. They also showed that cells infected with poliovirus changed characteristically. Enders called the changes *cytopathic effects* (CPE). This work paved the way for the development of poliovirus vaccines; and in the early 1950s, extensive study confirmed the efficacy of the Salk polio vaccine. In 1954, Enders, Robbins, and Weller were awarded the Nobel Prize.

In the 1960s, the spectrum of viral-related neurologic disorders broadened considerably when Gajdusek and others introduced the concept of slow virus infections. Such infections are known to cause several disorders in humans and animals and have been suspected to cause disorders such as multiple sclerosis (MS), amyotrophic lateral sclerosis (ALS), and certain dementias (Pick's and Alzheimer's diseases).

PATHOPHYSIOLOGY OF VIRAL CNS DISORDERS

Viruses appear to reach the CNS by several routes, but only in a few disorders is the exact route completely known. Figure 7.1 summarizes potential pathways of CNS viral infection and lists representative CNS disorders. CNS reactions to viral infection vary and reflect both host and viral factors. These varied reactions are in large part explained by what Johnson and others have called selective vulnerability of neural cells. The general principles of selective vulnerability imply that (1) various cell populations of the CNS differ in their susceptibility to viral infection and (2) viral effects vary among cell populations.

Host-cell reactions to viral infection are remarkably diverse (Figure 7.2). For example, cell lysis occurs in acute encephalitis, cell transformation may occur in experimental CNS tumors, and chronic cellular dysfunction presumably occurs during slow viral infections. Pathologic reactions to virus infection of the CNS include inflammation, necrosis, demyelination, spongy degeneration, and possibly malformation and neoplasia. These reactions may reflect the characteristics of the viral agent, the stage of host-cell development, the type of cell infected, or additional host factors such as immunologic competence. Thus, viruses can cause an acute disorder, such as meningitis, when infection is limited to the cells of the meninges, or they may cause a chronic demyelinating disorder when oligodendroglia (myelin-forming cells of the CNS) become infected.

DIAGNOSIS OF VIRAL CNS DISORDERS

Clinical features are rarely adequate for specific diagnosis of viral CNS disorders; therefore, neurodiagnostic and virologic laboratory procedures must be used. Neurodiagnostic procedures include electroencephalography (EEG), computed tomographic (CT) and isotope brain scanning, and examination of cerebrospinal fluid (CSF). In a few disorders, such as subacute sclerosing

Figure 7.1. Pathways of viral entry into the CNS. Primary viral replication may occur in skin, muscle, or gastrointestinal or respiratory tract.

Figure 7.2. Cellular reactions to CNS viral infection. Viruses can also infect and damage numerous additional cells within the CNS. These include meningeal cells (dura, arachnoid, pia), ependymal cells (cells lining CSF spaces) and endothelial cells of blood vessels.

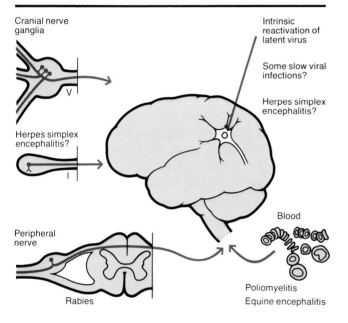

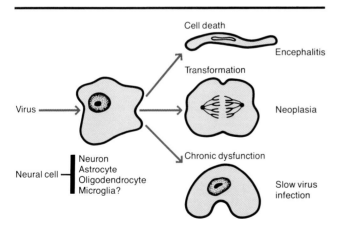

panencephalitis and herpes simplex encephalitis, the EEG and CT scan are characteristic. Although routine CSF profiles differentiate viral meningitis from bacterial meningitis (Table 7.1), the profiles rarely suggest a specific viral pathogen. However, more complicated CSF analyses, such as oligoclonal banding of CSF immunoglobulins and characterization of CSF antibodies, occasionally yield specific diagnoses (eg, subacute sclerosing panencephalitis). Confirmation of viral-caused CNS disorders usually requires isolation of the viral agent or demonstration of characteristic histopathologic features (Table 7.2 and Figure 7.3). In addition, immunofluorescent or immunoenzyme antibody techniques detect viral antigens in tissues and are useful in the rapid diagnosis of several viral CNS disorders, including herpes simplex encephalitis (Figure 7.4) and rabies.

CLINICAL SYNDROMES CAUSED BY VIRUSES

In general, numerous viruses can infect the CNS. The infections may spread to the CNS by several routes, may occur in many regions of the CNS, and consequently cause many different clinical syndromes. While vaccines prevent certain viral neurologic disorders, antiviral agents have been successful against few neurologic disorders caused by viruses.

Meningitis and encephalitis

Meningitis and encephalitis, common neurologic disorders, have been associated with numerous viral agents (Table 7.3). Considerable etiologic overlap occurs; consequently, a virus that causes meningitis in one person may produce encephalitis in another. Headache, stiff neck, fever, and vomiting are typically associated with meningitis, whereas altered consciousness, seizures, and focal neurologic deficits are associated with encephalitis. Occasional patients exhibit features of both meningitis and encephalitis (meningoencephalitis), and several nonviral disorders may also mimic these infections (Table 7.4).

Table 7.1.
Characteristics of cerebrospinal fluid (CSF)
in viral and bacterial meningitis

CSF	Viral meningitis	Bacterial meningitis
Glucose	Normal*	Low (<⅔ blood glucose)
Protein	Mild increase (50-150 mg/dl)	Usually very high (>200 mg/dl)
Cells	Moderate increase (0-500/mm³)	Usually very high (>500/mm³)
Cell type	Lymphocytes predominate†	Polymorphonuclear cells predominate

*Occasionally low in mumps or herpes simplex infections.

†Polymorphonuclear cells may predominate in the first 24 to 36 hours in patients with viral infections.

Table 7.2.
Viral inclusion bodies

INTRANUCLEAR

Type A

Herpes simplex virus
Cytomegalovirus (CMV)
Subacute sclerosing panencephalitis (measles virus)
Progressive multifocal leukoencephalitis (papovavirus)

Type B

Poliomyelitis (poliovirus)

INTRACYTOPLASMIC

CMV
Poliomyelitis
Rabies (Negri body)

Figure 7.3. Large single intranuclear (Cowdry type A) inclusion in a neuron infected with cytomegalovirus.

Figure 7.4. Positive fluorescent antibody (FA) staining in experimental HSV-1 infection.

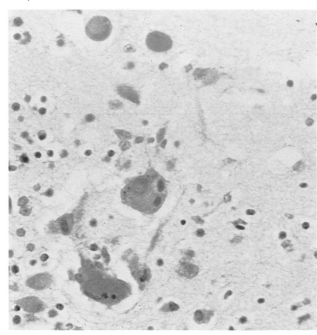

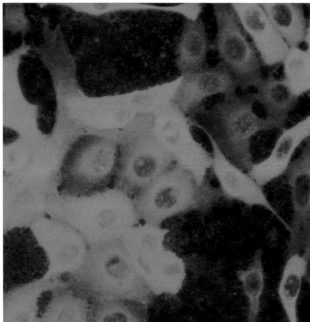

Table 7.3.
Viruses that cause encephalitis or meningitis

DNA VIRUSES
Herpes viruses
Herpes simplex viruses 1 and 2
Cytomegalovirus
Varicella-zoster

RNA VIRUSES
Togaviruses
Numerous species (eg, St. Louis, Western, and Eastern equine encephalitis)
Rubella virus

Picornaviruses (enteroviruses)
Polio virus
Echovirus
Coxsackieviruses A and B

Rhabdoviruses
Rabies
Marburg virus (extremely rare)

Paramyxoviruses
Measles
Mumps

Bunyaviruses
California encephalitis virus

Arenaviruses
Lymphocytic choriomeningitis virus

Reoviruses
Colorado tick fever

Table 7.4.
Disorders that mimic viral meningitis or encephalitis

Infectious disorders

Bacterial meningitis
Brain abscess
Syphilis
Tuberculous meningitis
Fungal meningitis (eg, cryptococcal)
Parasitic infections (eg, toxoplasmosis)
Amebic meningoencephalitis (eg, naeglerial)
Malaria *(Plasmodium falciparum)*
Rocky Mountain spotted fever
Mycoplasma pneumonia

Noninfectious disorders

Brain tumor
Stroke
Bechet's disease
Whipple's disease
Lead encephalopathy

Encephalitis caused by *herpes simplex virus* type 1 (HSV-1), the most common cause of sporadic encephalitis in humans, occurs worldwide and in all age groups. The hallmark of HSV-1 encephalitis is the presence of focal neurologic signs, which reflect the predilection of HSV-1 to involve unilaterally the medial temporal or inferior frontal regions of the cerebrum. The brain undergoes extensive focal necrosis with edema (Figure 7.5), and dramatic increases in intracranial pressure may occur. As a result, mortality is high; and sequelae are common.

The focal nature of HSV-1 encephalitis has intrigued neurologists and virologists for years. As a result, many theories have been proposed to explain the pathogenesis of the infection. Because the involved areas of the brain are closely associated with olfactory function, initially HSV-1 was suspected of entering the CNS via the nose and olfactory nerve. However, autopsy studies in humans demonstrated that HSV-1 latently infects the trigeminal (fifth cranial nerve) ganglion. This observation suggested the intriguing possibility that HSV-1 encephalitis might occur as a result of reactivation of HSV-1 and retrograde transmission to the CNS via the trigeminal nerve. This theory has been supported by anatomical evidence that the dura on the base of the brain near the involved frontal and temporal lobes is innervated by branches of the trigeminal nerve. However, viral reactivation in HSV-1 encephalitis has not been proven, and HSV-1 encephalitis may result from acute primary infection or reinfection with HSV-1.

The diagnosis of HSV-1 encephalitis is suggested by clinical features and supported by EEG findings or CT scan results or both. The EEG may show periodic complexes localized in the temporal lobe, and the CT scan often shows a focal, low-density lesion. HSV-1 encephalitis can be confirmed from brain biopsy specimens by (1) virus isolation; (2) demonstration of characteristic histopathologic features, such as inclusion bodies and

Figure 7.5. Necrosis of right temporal lobe secondary to herpes simplex type 1 encephalitis. Patient died despite surgical decompression of the infected temporal lobe and intravenous therapy with the antiviral agent adenine arabinoside.

Figure 7.6. Perivascular leukocyte infiltrate in herpes simplex type 1 encephalitis.

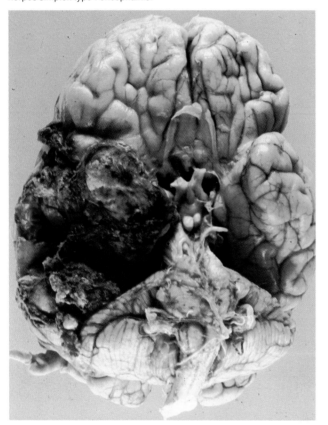

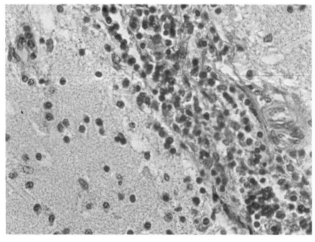

virus particles by light or electron microscopy (Figures 7.6 to 7.8); or (3) detection of HSV-1 antigen by immunofluorescent antibody techniques.

Studies of several antiviral agents have contributed greatly to the therapy of HSV-1 encephalitis. Although results with idoxuridine and cytarabine were disappointing, therapy with another purine analogue, vidarabine, has improved the outcome for patients who have encephalitis caused by HSV-1. Mortality has declined significantly from 70% to 28% in patients who were treated with vidarabine for biopsy-proven, HSV-1 encephalitis. The incidence of neurologic sequelae has also declined. The continuing development of antiviral agents may result in therapy that provides even greater reduction in the morbidity and mortality caused by HSV-1 encephalitis.

Other herpes viruses, notably HSV-2 in neonates and cytomegalovirus (CMV), may also occasionally cause encephalitis or meningitis. In addition, several disorders can mimic HSV-1 encephalitis (Table 7.5).

Although *rabies* virus infection in humans rarely occurs in developed countries, rabies continues to be an important viral neurologic disorder. Rabies virus can infect nearly all mammals; many species, notably skunks, bats, and foxes, serve as reservoirs for the virus. Because of widespread vaccination of domestic animals, most cases of rabies in humans result from bites by infected wild animals whose saliva contains the virus. After a variable period of latency, the virus enters the peripheral nerve, which transmits the virus to the CNS, where the virus replicates and produces encephalitis. The incubation period, usually 30 to 60 days, varies widely and has been as long as one year. Initial symptoms include pain near the wound, fever, and headache. Behavioral changes and hydrophobia, caused by spasms of pharyngeal muscles, are hallmark features. Typically, the disease progresses rapidly and with rare exception results in death within a few days.

A brain infected with rabies virus shows typical fea-

Figure 7.7. Intranuclear inclusion bodies in a brain biopsy specimen from a patient with herpes simplex encephalitis.

Figure 7.8. Neuron with numerous intranuclear virus particles in experimental herpes simplex type 1 encephalitis.

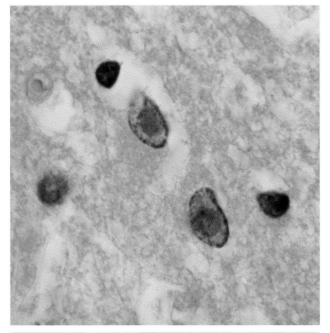

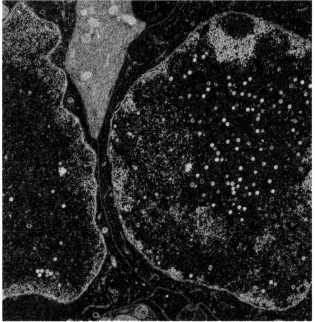

Table 7.5.
Disorders that mimic HSV-1 encephalitis

Infectious
Brain abscess
Encephalitis caused by mumps virus, coxsackievirus, Epstein-Barr virus, St. Louis equine encephalitis virus, California encephalitis virus, lymphocytic choriomeningitis virus
Tuberculosis
Toxoplasma gondii infection
Reye's syndrome

Noninfectious
Vascular disease
Tumor
Toxic encephalopathy

tures of encephalitis—microglial proliferation and perivascular cellular infiltrates—and characteristic intracytoplasmic viral inclusions, or Negri bodies. The rabies virus can be isolated from brain tissue and, less often, from saliva. Immunofluorescence, currently the diagnostic method of choice, can rapidly demonstrate rabies viral antigen in neural tissues.

Because no effective antiviral therapy for symptomatic rabies virus infection exists, protocols for suspected rabies exposure should be followed closely. Currently, postexposure therapy includes vigorous wound cleansing and, when indicated, combinations of vaccine and antiserum (Figure 7.9).

Poliomyelitis (polio), a crippling disease once a source of considerable mortality and morbidity, particularly in children, has been virtually eradicated in developed countries. The poliovirus, appropriately classified as an enterovirus, is acquired orally and undergoes primary replication in the oral and intestinal mucosa. This primary phase of infection and transient viremia are typically associated with signs of upper-respiratory and gastrointestinal illness. In nonimmune individuals, persistent viremia develops, the virus enters the CNS, and neurologic complications follow. Symptoms at this stage include fever and headache. Infection of the motor

84

Figure 7.9. Clinical approach to possible rabies exposure.

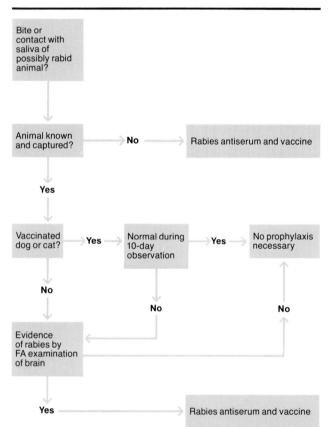

neurons (anterior horn cells) may result in paralysis of swallowing, breathing, and limb motor function. Trauma, pregnancy, and tonsillectomy are host factors associated with increased frequency and severity of paralysis.

In the United States, the development of two vaccines, an inactivated virus vaccine (Salk) in 1954 and a live-attenuated virus vaccine (Sabin) in the 1960s, dramatically reduced the annual incidence of polio from nearly 30,000 cases in 1955 to less than 25 cases in 1970. Currently, most cases of polio in the United States occur in people who have not been immunized or as a consequence of polio vaccine administration.

As poliovirus infection disappeared, two other enteroviruses, coxsackie and echoviruses, were discovered. These viruses can cause several neurologic disorders, including aseptic meningitis, encephalitis, and a paralytic disease resembling polio.

Several viruses that cause encephalitis in humans can be transmitted by *arthropod vectors*, such as mosquitoes and ticks. These viruses, formerly classified as arboviruses (ie, <u>ar</u>thropod <u>bo</u>rne viruses), are currently classified as togaviruses (Table 7.6). Encephalitis caused by such viruses usually occurs in local epidemics; because of the life cycle of the vector, the disease characteristically occurs in spring or summer. The virus is contained in the saliva of the biting insect and is inoculated into the blood or lymph of the host (typically horses or humans). The virus then replicates in muscle tissue and in reticuloendothelial tissue (lymph node or spleen), and presumably it reaches the CNS hematogenously. Togavirus encephalitis, although uncommon, tends to be more severe than encephalitis caused by other viral agents. The diagnosis, based on clinical features of the disease, season, and geographic location, can be supported by serologic tests (complement fixation or hemagglutination inhibition), which demonstrate a rise in antibody titers. The virus can be isolated from neural tissue and, less commonly, from blood and cerebrospinal fluid.

Slow virus infections

Several neurodegenerative disorders, previously of unknown etiology, are now known to be caused by viruses or by viral-like agents (Table 7.7). These disorders, termed *slow virus infections of the nervous system*, illustrate a novel concept of disease pathogenesis. The concept evolved during the second half of the 20th century.

Features characteristic of slow virus infections are (1) a long incubation period (months to years), (2) subacute deterioration usually resulting in death in weeks to months, and (3) involvement of one organ system, usually the CNS.

Conventional viruses and unconventional virus-like agents are responsible for these uniformly fatal disorders. The unconventional agents exhibit unique physical and biologic properties (Table 7.8). Unlike conventional viruses, the unconventional agents do not incite an inflammatory response in the brain, do not cause CSF pleocytosis or protein elevation, and do not stimulate an immune response. Unconventional agents do, however, produce a characteristic neuropathologic change, status spongiosus, which consists of glial scarring (gliosis) and vacuolation of nerve cells and axons.

Kuru was the first neurodegenerative disorder to be associated with a slow virus infection in humans, and it is the prototype of spongiform encephalopathies caused by unconventional viral agents. Kuru, which was extensively studied by Gajdusek, occurs in the Fore natives of New Guinea. The disorder begins insidiously, causes tremor and cerebellar signs, and invariably progresses to death within one year of onset. The kuru agent, although incompletely characterized, has been isolated from the brain tissue of kuru patients and has been successfully transmitted to several experimental animals, including minks, ferrets, and old- and new-world monkeys. Transmission of the disease in humans occurs as a result of ritualistic cannibalism. During the past decade, the incidence of kuru has diminished as cannibalism has declined.

Table 7.6.
Togaviruses that cause CNS infection

Alphaviruses	Vector
Eastern equine encephalitis virus	Mosquito
Western equine encephalitis virus	Mosquito
Venezuelan equine encephalitis virus	Mosquito
Flaviviruses	
St. Louis encephalitis virus	Mosquito
Japanese encephalitis virus	Mosquito
Murray Valley encephalitis virus	Mosquito
Russian spring-summer encephalitis viruses (14 viruses)	Tick
Rio Bravo virus (bat salivary gland virus)	Unknown

Table 7.7.
Slow viral infections of humans and other animals

CAUSED BY CONVENTIONAL AGENTS
Humans
Subacute sclerosing panencephalitis (measles virus)
Progressive rubella panencephalitis (rubella virus)
Progressive multifocal leukoencephalopathy (papovaviruses)

Other animals
Visna (retrovirus)

CAUSED BY UNCONVENTIONAL AGENTS
Humans
Kuru
Creutzfeldt-Jakob disease

Other animals
Scrapie
Transmissible mink encephalopathy

Table 7.8.
Properties of unconventional viral agents

Long incubation period
No inflammatory response
No cytopathic effect in infected cells in vitro
No virus-like particles or inclusion bodies
No interferon production or sensitivity
No infectious nucleic acid
No antigenicity
Resistant to formaldehyde, proteases, nucleases, heat (80°C), ultraviolet radiation, ultrasonic energy, and ionizing radiation

Figure 7.10. Coronal section through the brain of a patient who had Creutzfeldt-Jakob disease. The brain shows mild cortical atrophy and hydrocephalus *ex vacuo* (enlarged cerebral ventricles secondary to loss of brain substance).

Figure 7.11. Status spongiosus in Creutzfeldt-Jakob disease.

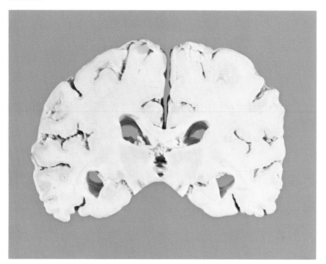

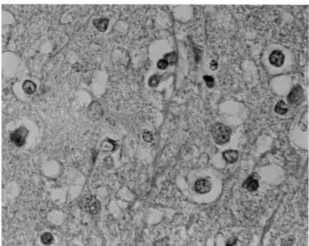

Creutzfeldt-Jakob disease (CJD), a rare spongiform encephalopathy caused by an unconventional agent, occurs worldwide. Although approximately 10% of cases appear to have an autosomal dominant pattern of inheritance, most cases are sporadic. The neuropathologic features of CJD parallel those of scrapie (a slow virus disease of sheep) and kuru. Unlike scrapie and kuru, however, CJD's major clinical manifestations – myoclonus (sudden muscle contractions) and rapidly evolving dementia (loss of memory and intellect) – reflect prominent involvement of the cerebral cortex (Figures 7.10 and 7.11). Disease transmission between humans has been reported, and the disease has been transmitted to several species of experimental animals.

Unlike kuru and CJD, *subacute sclerosing panencephalitis* (SSPE) and *progressive rubella panencephalitis* (PRPE) represent slow viral CNS infections caused by conventional agents, namely, the measles virus (in SSPE) and the rubella virus (in PRPE). These disorders are rare – one case of SSPE occurs per one million cases of measles. PRPE and SSPE usually occur in childhood or adolescence, and they bear several clinical and pathologic similarities. Infection usually occurs early in life; in the usual case of PRPE, infection occurs in utero. After a long latent period, which for SSPE averages five years, the infected individual loses motor and mental skills and may develop myoclonic seizures. SSPE and PRPE typically lead to severe debility for several months or until the patient dies. Although diagnosis of early or atypical cases may be difficult, SSPE is usually associated with a characteristic electroencephalogram pattern. Diagnosis of SSPE or PRPE can be supported by demonstrating elevated CSF antibody to measles or rubella; diagnosis can be confirmed by characteristic histopathologic changes in brain tissue. In addition, CSF typically shows oligoclonal IgG bands (Figure 7.12) and markedly increased IgG levels. Despite studies of antiviral therapy, no effective therapy for either SSPE or PRPE exists.

Figure 7.12. Oligoclonal IgG bands in SSPE.
A. Normal cerebrospinal fluid (CSF) electrophoretic pattern. *B.* Abnormal oligoclonal IgG bands (arrow) in the CSF of a 20-year-old patient with SSPE. This patient also exhibited an abnormally elevated CSF level of measles antibody.

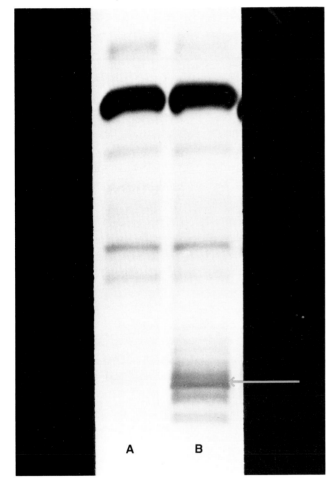

A   B

Several questions about the mechanisms by which measles and rubella virus cause SSPE and PRPE remain unanswered. How do the viruses become and remain latent or persistent? What triggers the subsequent clinical deterioration? In the case of SSPE, two hypotheses of its etiology have been proposed: (1) an atypical or mutant virus causes SSPE in a normal host, or (2) normal measles virus causes SSPE in an immunologically abnormal host. Although considerable experimental evidence has accumulated in support of these hypotheses,

neither has gained universal acceptance. Differences between some wild-type and SSPE measles virus strains have been described, and host immune factors clearly appear to be important in the persistence of measles virus infection. The observation that SSPE patients lack antibody to a specific measles virus protein, the M protein, may provide a clue to the pathogenesis of this devastating disorder.

Progressive multifocal leukoencephalopathy (PML) is a rare CNS demyelinating disorder caused by infection of oligodendrocytes with a papovavirus, a conventional viral agent. PML typically affects a patient with Hodgkin's disease or leukemia but may occur in other immunoincompetent patients. A papovavirus, JC virus has been recovered from most patients who have PML; in some cases, viruses similar to simian virus 40 (SV40) have been isolated. As in SSPE and PRPE, many questions regarding the pathogenesis of PML remain unanswered.

DISEASES OF SUSPECTED OR POSSIBLE VIRAL ETIOLOGY
Viruses presumably play a role in several additional disorders of the nervous system. The discovery of slow virus infections has suggested that other chronic neurologic disorders, notably multiple sclerosis, may be caused by viruses or viral-like agents.

Multiple sclerosis
Multiple sclerosis (MS) is the prototype of demyelinating disorders of the central nervous system. The disease typically begins in young adults who experience clinical exacerbations and remissions over several years. Because foci of demyelination (plaques) may be widespread in the CNS (Figure 7.13), the clinical manifestations of the disorder are protean. The ante mortem diagnosis of MS rests ultimately upon the clinical features of the illness; however, most patients who have MS have

Figure 7.13. Coronal section through the brain of a patient who had multiple sclerosis. This section shows numerous periventricular plaques, a pathologic feature typical of demyelinating disorders. The plaques are the darker, myelin-deficient areas in the white matter adjacent to the lateral ventricles.

Figure 7.14. Fatty change in liver during Reye's syndrome.

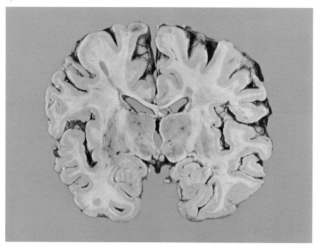

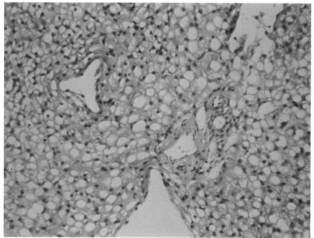

elevated CSF IgG-to-albumin ratios and oligoclonal IgG bands in CSF.

Despite nearly a century of medical research, the etiology of MS remains an enigma; both hereditary and environmental elements have been implicated. Studies supporting an immunogenetic etiology demonstrate an association between the disease and certain histocompatibility antigens and defects in immune function.

Alternatively, considerable circumstantial evidence favors the hypothesis that an environmental agent, possibly a virus, is a major etiologic factor. The results of several epidemiologic studies suggest that exposure to certain environmental conditions during childhood or adolescence may precede the development of MS. Studies of the worldwide geographic distribution of MS show an increasing incidence with increasing latitude. Immigrants retain the MS risk of their birthplace if they migrate after age 15 but assume the risk of their new residence if they migrate before age 15. Occasional MS epidemics, the most notable of which occurred in the Faroe Islands after World War II, support the hypothesis that MS is an acquired, possibly transmissible, disease.

Numerous serologic and pathologic attempts to associate MS with a specific viral agent have been unsuccessful. Although several animal models of CNS demyelination have been developed (Table 7.9), none produces MS as it occurs in humans. MS may be caused by an as yet undefined agent or may result from an immunologic process triggered by any of several viral agents. In summary, MS remains a puzzling and challenging disorder of the nervous system, and uncovering its cause would represent one of the greatest triumphs of neurovirology.

Guillain-Barré syndrome

Guillain-Barré syndrome (GBS), a demyelinating disorder of peripheral nerves, is characterized by progressive motor weakness and loss of deep tendon reflexes. Prominent associated features include mild sensory complaints, involvement of cranial nerves, classical bilateral facial paralysis, and autonomic nerve dysfunction. Although most patients with GBS report an antecedent viral illness, the role of viruses in the pathogenesis of this disease is unclear. Examination of peripheral nerves reveals foci of inflammatory cells and demyelination, supporting the concept that GBS may be immunologically and, possibly, virologically mediated. Viral agents associated with GBS include cytomegalovirus, Epstein-Barr virus, coxsackievirus B, and, less commonly, varicella and influenza viruses.

Reye's syndrome

Reye's syndrome was recognized as a clinical entity in the early 1960s. Although no direct viral involvement of the nervous system occurs in Reye's syndrome, viruses appear to play a major role in its pathogenesis. The disease typically develops in a young child who has recently had a minor viral illness, usually of the upper respiratory tract. Severe vomiting and progressive loss of consciousness ensue. These symptoms are accompanied by widespread metabolic alterations, notably hypoglycemia, and by severe hepatic dysfunction with hyperammoniemia, elevated liver enzyme levels (SGOT and SGPT), and depletion of liver-associated clotting factors. The viscera show characteristic fatty degeneration (Figure 7.14), and the brain exhibits massive cerebral edema – the major cause of death in Reye's syndrome. Viruses associated with this disorder include coxsackievirus B, varicella-zoster, parainfluenza, and echoviruses. Local epidemics of Reye's syndrome have also occurred during outbreaks of influenza A and B.

Tumors, malformations, and mental retardation

Numerous neurologic disorders of undetermined etiology may ultimately be found to be caused by viruses. Such disorders include brain tumors, congenital malformations, and some types of mental retardation. Viruses such as cytomegalovirus and rubella have already been linked to microcephaly, hearing loss, and mental retardation. Mumps virus causes aqueductal stenosis and acquired hydrocephalus in humans and experimental animals. Although human brain tumors have not been conclusively associated with viral infection, several viruses produce cerebral tumors in experimental animals (Table 7.10). Thus, our understanding of the role of viruses in the etiology of these disorders will likely be greatly expanded.

Table 7.9.
Animal models of CNS demyelination

Mouse hepatitis virus (JHM virus)
Theiler's murine encephalomyelitis virus
Canine distemper virus
Experimental allergic encephalomyelitis (nonviral)

Table 7.10.
Virus-induced brain tumors in animals

Virus	Tumor	Host
Adenoviruses		
Types 12, 18	Sarcoma	Hamster
Simian	Sarcoma	Hamster
Type 12	Neuroblastoma	Rat
Type 12	Medulloblastoma	Mouse
Papovaviruses		
JC	Meningioma, medulloblastoma	Hamster
JC	Glioma	Monkey
BK	Choroid plexus papilloma	Hamster
SV-40	Choroid plexus papilloma	Hamster
Oncornaviruses		
Avian sarcoma	Sarcoma	Chicken, turkey, rabbit, dog, rat, monkey
Avian sarcoma	Glioma	Hamster, mouse, rat, guinea pig, dog, cat
Murine sarcoma	Meningioma, glioma	Rat
Simian sarcoma	Glioma	Marmoset

Selected
References

Baringer JR: Herpes simplex virus infection of nervous tissue in animals and man. *Prog Med Virol* 20:1-26, 1975.

Bell WE, McCormick WF: *Neurologic Infections in Children,* ed 2. Philadelphia, WB Saunders Co, 1981, pp 285-492.

Bigner DD, Pegram CN: Virus-induced experimental brain tumors and putative associations of viruses with human brain tumors: A review. *Adv Neurol* 15:57-83, 1976.

Brooks BR, Jubelt B, Swarz JR, et al: Slow viral infections. *Annu Rev Neurosci* 2:309-340, 1979.

Cook SD, Dowling PC: Multiple sclerosis and viruses: An overview. *Neurology* 30:80-91, 1980.

Davis LE, Johnson RT: An explanation for the localization of herpes simplex encephalitis? *Ann Neurol* 5:2-5, 1979.

Dowling PC, Cook SD: Role of infection in Guillain-Barré syndrome: Laboratory confirmation of herpesviruses in 41 cases. *Ann Neurol* 9 (suppl): 44-55, 1981.

Dupont JR, Earle KM: Human rabies encephalitis: A study of forty-nine fatal cases with a review of the literature. *Neurology* 15:1023-1034, 1965.

Gajdusek CD: Unconventional viruses and the origin and disappearance of Kuru. *Science* 197:943-960, 1977.

Ginsberg HS: Togaviruses, in Dulbecco R, Ginsberg HS (eds): *Virology.* Hagerstown, Md, Harper & Row, Publishers Inc, 1980, pp 1177-1196.

Griffith JF, Ch'ien LT: Viral infections of the nervous system, in Galasso GJ, Merigan TC, Buchanan RA (eds): *Antiviral Agents and Viral Diseases of Man.* New York, Raven Press, 1979, pp 492-539.

Haller JS: Enigmatic encephalopathy of Reye's syndrome. *Hosp Pract* 10(2):91-99, 1975.

Johnson RT: Selective vulnerability of neural cells to viral infections. *Brain* 103:447-472, 1980.

Johnson RT, Griffin DE: Pathogenesis of viral infections, in Vinken PJ, Bruyn GW (eds): *Handbook of Clinical Neurology.* Amsterdam, Elsevier North-Holland Publishing Co, 1978, vol 34, pp 15-37.

Kurtzke JF: Epidemiologic contributions to multiple sclerosis: An overview. *Neurology* 30:61-79, 1980.

Masters CL, Harris JO, Gajdusek DC, et al: Creutzfeldt-Jakob disease: Patterns of worldwide occurrence and the significance of familial and sporadic clustering. *Ann Neurol* 5:177-188, 1979.

Narayan O, Penney JB, Johnson RT, et al: Etiology of progressive multifocal leukoencephalopathy: Identification of papovavirus. *N Engl J Med* 289:1278-1282, 1973.

Paul JR: *A History of Poliomyelitis.* New Haven, Yale University Press, 1971.

Payne FE, Baublis JV, Itabashi HH: Isolation of measles virus from cell cultures of brain from a patient with subacute sclerosing panencephalitis. *N Engl J Med* 281:585-589, 1969.

Townsend JJ, Baringer JR, Wolinsky JS, et al: Progressive rubella panencephalitis: Late onset after congenital rubella. *N Engl J Med* 292:990-993, 1975.

Weller TH: The cytomegaloviruses: Ubiquitous agents with protean clinical manifestations. *N Engl J Med* 285:203-214, 267-274, 1971.

Whitley RJ, Seng-Jaw S, Hirsch MS, et al: Herpes simplex encephalitis: Vidarabine therapy and diagnostic problems. *N Engl J Med* 304:313-318, 1981.

Viral Infections of the Fetus and Newborn

Lawrence R. Stanberry, MD, PhD

Assistant Professor
Division of Infectious Diseases
Department of Pediatrics
The University of Cincinnati
and Children's Hospital Medical Center
Cincinnati, OH 45229

Lowell A. Glasgow, MD[†]

Professor and Chairman
Department of Pediatrics
The University of Utah and Primary
Children's Medical Centers
Salt Lake City, UT 84132

[†]Doctor Glasgow died February 4, 1982.

Only a few of the hundreds of viruses to which humans are constantly exposed produce disease in the fetus and newborn. The extent of injury caused by a perinatal viral infection is determined both by the type of virus and the stage of development of the fetus. For example, viral infection that occurs in early gestation during critical phases of organ development may cause significant fetal malformations, whereas the same infection in late gestation may produce no apparent damage. Table 8.1 lists the effects of certain viral infections in the fetus and newborn.

The incidence and severity of perinatal viral infections are influenced primarily by maternal age, gestational age of the fetus, existence of a vaccine, occurrence of an epidemic, and socioeconomic status (Table 8.2). In some populations, the incidence of perinatal viral infections in all live newborns may be as great as 6% to 8%, 15 to 40 times the incidence of systemic bacterial infection in neonates. Table 8.3 shows the approximate incidence of perinatal viral infections in pregnant women and their offspring.

An understanding of the differences between viral and bacterial disease and an understanding of virus-host interactions in the fetus and newborn is necessary to (1) accurately diagnose acute viral infections, (2) consider all viral infections that may exist in a dysmorphic infant, (3) anticipate the effect of perinatal viral infections on subsequent growth and development, and (4) rapidly provide effective antiviral chemotherapy when indicated.

PATHOGENESIS OF PERINATAL VIRAL INFECTIONS

Conceptually, perinatal viral infections may be divided into three categories: (1) those contracted in utero (congenital), (2) those contracted during delivery (natal), and (3) those contracted in the neonatal period (postnatal) (Table 8.4 and Figures 8.1a to 8.1c).

Although congenital viral infections result from maternal viral infections, most maternal viral infections do not result in a systemic illness, viremia, and fetal involvement (Figure 8.1a). However, if in utero infection does occur, it may cause fetal death, premature birth, intrauterine growth retardation, or persistent postnatal infection and developmental malformations, such as microcephaly, chorioretinitis, congenital heart defects, and limb hypoplasia.

Viruses that multiply in the rapidly proliferating fetal tissue may destroy cells or alter cell function. The more lytic viruses (eg, measles or vaccinia) can result in fetal death. The less destructive viruses (eg, cytomegalovirus or rubella) may not produce death; however, if virus-cell interactions occur at a critical phase in organ development, congenital anomalies may result.

Natal viral infections result from fetal contact with a virus at the time of birth. Sources of such viruses are (1) contaminated genital secretions (eg, herpes simplex virus), (2) stool (eg, enterovirus), and (3) maternal blood during acute or chronic viremia (eg, hepatitis B) (Figure 8.1b). Although the newborn may, on occasion, be highly susceptible, severity of disease may vary from asymptomatic or mild illness to disseminated disease with extensive organ involvement and death. Virus incubation periods vary and may range from a few days, as with herpes simplex virus or enteroviruses, to weeks, as with cytomegalovirus.

Postnatal viral infections result from viral exposure of newborns during the first month after birth (Figure 8.1c). In addition to maternal sources (eg, herpes simplex vi-

Table 8.1.
Effect of viral infection in the fetus and newborn

Virus	Fetal death	Prematurity	Intrauterine growth retardation	Intrauterine infection		Postnatal infection		Primary congenital defect
				Acute	Persistent	Acute	Persistent	
Rubella	+	+	+	+	+	−	+	Cataract, deafness, heart defect
Cytomegalovirus	−	+	+	+	+	+	+	Microcephaly, deafness
Herpes simplex	+	+	+	+	+	+	+	Microcephaly
Varicella-zoster	−	+	+	+	+	+	+	Hypoplasia of limbs
Echo	−	−	−	+	−	+	−	−
Coxsackie	+	−	−	+	−	+	−	Heart defect?
Polio	+	+	−	+	−	−	−	−
Hepatitis B	−	+	−	−	+	+	+	−
Respiratory syncytial	−	−	−	−	−	+	−	−

+Effect proven   −No known effect   ?Effect suspected

Table 8.2.
Factors that influence the incidence and severity of perinatal viral infections

Maternal infection
Maternal immunity
Maternal age
Gestational age of fetus
Socioeconomic status
Geographic location
Season
Presence of an epidemic
Existence of a vaccine
Frequency of neonatal blood transfusion
Incidence of nosocomial spread

Table 8.4.
Acquisition of perinatal viral disease

Virus	Congenital	Natal	Postnatal
Rubella	+*	−	Rare
Cytomegalovirus	+	+*	+
Herpes simplex	+	+*	+
Varicella-zoster	+*	Rare	Rare
Enteroviruses	+	+*	+
Hepatitis B	+	+*	+

*Primary time of acquisition

Table 8.3.
Approximate incidence of viral infections in pregnant women and their offspring

Virus	Maternal incidence (per 1000 pregnancies)	Neonatal incidence (per 1000 live births)
Rubella		
Epidemic	20–40	3–7
Nonepidemic	0.1–20	0.1–0.7
Postvaccine	0.03–0.7	0.03–0.2
Cytomegalovirus		
During pregnancy	20–70	6–34
At delivery	30–130	20–70
Herpes simplex	1–10	0.03–0.5
Varicella-zoster	Uncommon	Rare
Enteroviruses	90	Uncommon
Hepatitis B	2–30	0–7

94

Figures 8.1a-8.1c. Pathogenesis of viral infections in the fetus and the newborn.

Figure 8.1a. Pathogenesis of congenital viral infection.

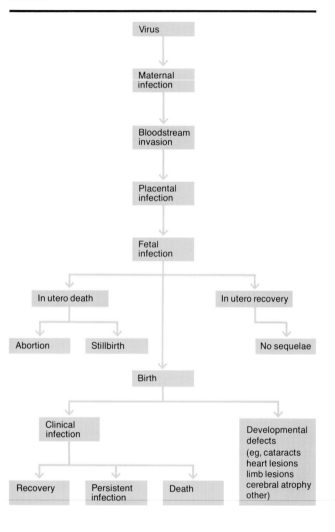

Figure 8.1b. Pathogenesis of natal viral infection.

Figure 8.1c. Pathogenesis of postnatal viral infection.

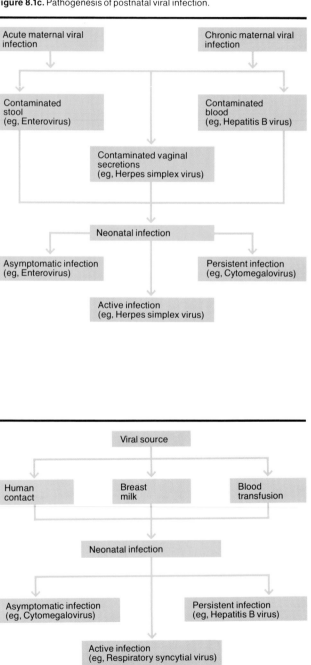

rus, enteroviruses, cytomegalovirus, and hepatitis B virus), postnatal viral infection may be acquired from hospital patients, hospital personnel, or family members (herpes simplex virus, enteroviruses, and respiratory syncytial virus), breast milk (cytomegalovirus and hepatitis B), or blood transfusion (cytomegalovirus and hepatitis B). Most postnatal infections are self-limited. However, respiratory syncytial virus and herpes simplex virus may produce long-term sequelae; cytomegalovirus and hepatitis B may produce chronic infection; and respiratory syncytial virus, enteroviruses, herpes simplex virus, and cytomegalovirus may cause death.

DIAGNOSIS OF PERINATAL VIRAL INFECTIONS

Clinical manifestations of congenital viral infection include small infant size (intrauterine growth retardation), seizures, pneumonitis, and hepatosplenomegaly with or without hepatitis, icterus, and purpura. All are usually evident at birth. Developmental anomalies, such as microcephaly, congenital heart defects, limb hypoplasia, or eye lesions, such as cataracts, microphthalmia, and chorioretinitis, may be present. Perinatal viral infection may be suggested by maternal history of infection, aberrant clinical features, abnormal laboratory findings, or other abnormalities the infant may exhibit while in the hospital nursery. Features of acute viral infections in neonates resemble those of bacterial sepsis and include temperature instability, irritability, lethargy, poor feeding, seizures, hypertonia or hypotonia, meningitis, skin rashes, conjunctivitis, myocarditis, hepatitis, and pneumonitis.

Laboratory tests designed to identify specific etiologic agents (Table 8.5) are useful in making a diagnosis. Virus isolation is the preferred method; however, when this method is not available, histologic examination or serologic tests may suggest the diagnosis. Newer techniques include detection of viral particles by electron micros-

copy and identification of viral antigens by immunologic methods such as radioimmunoassay (RIA) or enzyme-linked immunosorbent assay (ELISA).

RUBELLA

Intrauterine rubella infection is the classic congenital viral disease, and characteristics of virus-host interaction illustrate important concepts of fetal virus infections. Risk to the fetus is greatest during early pregnancy, especially the first three months, which is the critical phase of organ development. Fetal damage may also occur in the second trimester. Perhaps 65% of infants who have proven congenital rubella are asymptomatic at birth; however, subtle defects or long-term sequelae have been detected in more than 90% of these children by the time they are 12 years old.

In symptomatic infants, the chief abnormalities are cataracts and heart defects. Other common findings are eye lesions, meningitis, encephalitis, hepatosplenomegaly, bone lesions, limb hypoplasia, and purpuric or petechial rashes associated with thrombocytopenia. Late signs of congenital rubella, such as hearing loss or psychomotor retardation, may not have been recognized initially; or the signs may have resulted from progressive disease, such as thyroiditis, diabetes mellitus, or chronic encephalopathy. Clinical manifestations of congenital rubella are listed in Table 8.6.

The prognosis for severely affected infants is poor, and mortality is particularly high the first year. Survivors generally have significant sequelae, including hearing loss, cardiovascular and urogenital disorders, endocrine disturbances, neurologic deficits, and psychiatric disorders.

No antiviral therapy is available for the treatment of congenital rubella. Management is largely supportive, and the best treatment plans use a multidisciplinary approach that includes input from physicians, special educators, social workers, psychologists, and speech

Table 8.5.
Laboratory diagnosis of perinatal viral disease

Virus isolation	IgM-specific antiviral antibody
Virus particle detection	IgG antiviral antibody
Virus antigen detection	Quantitative IgM antibody level
Viral DNA detection	Histopathology

Table 8.6.
Manifestations of congenital rubella

General
Intrauterine growth retardation
Postnatal growth retardation
Failure to thrive

Eye
Cataracts
Retinopathy
Microphthalmia
Glaucoma

Heart
Patent ductus arteriosus
Pulmonary arterial hypoplasia
Coarctation of the aorta

Ear
Sensorineural deafness

Central nervous system
Encephalitis
Meningitis
Microcephaly
Psychomotor retardation
Speech and learning disabilities
Behaviour disorders
Late-onset encephalopathy

Skin
Purpuric or petechial rash
Chronic rubelliform rash

Blood
Thrombocytopenia
Anemia
Leukopenia

Bones
Osteopathy
Radiolucencies

Lungs
Interstitial pneumonitis

Genitourinary system
Undescended testicles
Polycystic kidney
Hypospadias

Gastrointestinal system
Hepatitis
Intestinal atresia
Chronic diarrhea

Endocrine system
Diabetes mellitus (early onset)
Thyroiditis

and hearing personnel. Neonates who have congenital rubella remain chronically infected and may excrete virus for an extended period of time. They are particularly contagious during the first year of life; and during this time, appropriate precautions should be used to prevent transmission of the disease to others.

Since licensure in the United States in 1969 of the live attenuated rubella vaccine, the estimated incidence of congenital rubella has decreased from three to seven cases per 1000 live births during the 1964 epidemic to approximately 0.1 case per 1000 live births in 1978. Continued surveillance is necessary to determine whether the current program of immunizing infants is adequate for maintaining immunity during childbearing years and for preventing congenital rubella in future generations.

CYTOMEGALOVIRUS

Cytomegalovirus (CMV) is the most frequently occurring perinatal viral infection. The incidence of congenital CMV is one to two cases per 100 live births, and the incidence of natal CMV is four to ten cases per 100 live births. Postnatal CMV infections also occur frequently and may occasionally be iatrogenic. Ninety percent to 95% of all infants who have congenitally or natally acquired CMV infections are asymptomatic in the neonatal period, but many manifest neurologic sequelae in later childhood. Clinical manifestations of CMV infection are summarized in Table 8.7.

Congenital CMV infection may result from a primary infection, reinfection, or reactivation of a latent infection in the mother. A primary CMV infection does not confer lasting immunity. To the contrary, CMV may establish a latent infection, which despite adequate humoral immunity may be reactivated, resulting in viral shedding and transmission to the fetus or neonate. Profound congenital CMV infection (cytomegalic inclusion disease) is characterized by retarded intrauterine growth, microcephaly, jaundice, thrombocytopenic purpura (blueberry-muffin appearance) (Figure 8.2), hepatospleno-megaly, and severe CNS damage. Congenital CMV infections have been associated with primary CMV infection in the mother early in pregnancy. Congenital infection also occurs in infants of immune women harboring latent virus; reactivation of latent virus may occur and does so most commonly late in pregnancy. During the third trimester, about 13% of pregnant infected women shed the virus from the cervix. The infected infants shed virus, but they rarely have clinical cytomegalic inclusion disease; hence, the severity of congenital CMV infection appears to vary according to the stage of pregnancy during which the mother's infection is active and to her immune status before pregnancy.

Natally acquired CMV infection results from passage through an infected birth canal. These infections may be characterized by pneumonia, hepatosplenomegaly with or without hepatitis, chronic gastrointestinal disturbances, or failure to thrive. About 40% of infants born to women who have CMV in the genital tract will acquire the infection.

CMV may be transmitted to neonates by breast milk, blood transfusions, or exposure to persons with naso-pharyngeal shedding. Most cases of postnatally acquired CMV are asymptomatic. CMV transmitted by blood transfusion to high-risk neonates (eg, premature infants) results in a syndrome characterized by hepatospleno-megaly, septic appearance, deterioration of respiratory status, gray pallor, and atypical lymphocytosis. In one series of cases, three of 16 infants who had this syndrome died.

While most infants who have congenital CMV infection are clinically asymptomatic in the neonatal period, substantial evidence suggests that later in childhood many will manifest a broad spectrum of neurologic deficits. Obvious abnormalities may include microcephaly, mental retardation, deafness, spasticity, hypotonia, or strabismus. Subtler abnormalities include varying de-

Figure 8.2. Neonate with congenital cytomegalo-virus infection.

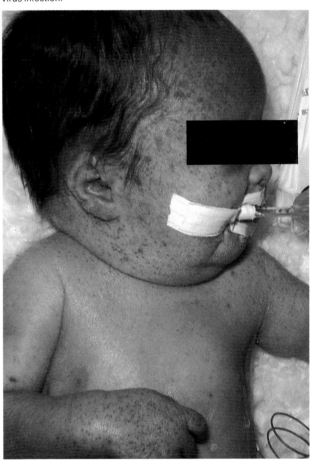

Table 8.7.
Manifestations of perinatal cytomegalovirus infection

Congenital	Natal
Low birth weight	Failure to thrive
Hepatomegaly	Hepatomegaly
Splenomegaly	Splenomegaly
Jaundice	Pneumonitis
Petechiae, purpura	Anemia
Pneumonitis	Chronic gastroenteritis
Microcephaly	
Hydrocephalus	**Postnatal**
Cerebral calcification	Pneumonitis
Deafness	Hepatomegaly
Blindness	Gray pallor
Chorioretinitis	Splenomegaly

grees of hearing loss, speech and learning defects, attention deficits, intelligence quotients lower than those of siblings, and behavioral disorders (Table 8.8). Each year in the United States, an estimated 33,000 infants are born with CMV, and this virus appears to be a significant cause of mental retardation, deafness, and perhaps learning and behavioral disorders.

No effective antiviral chemotherapy for CMV infection exists. Idoxuridine, floxuridine, the arabinosides, interferon inducers, and human interferon transiently suppress urinary excretion of virus in patients who have active CMV infection, but the drugs and interferons do not otherwise alter the course of the illness. Drug studies directed toward inapparent CMV infection in infants in whom antiviral drugs might prevent central nervous system damage should be considered.

Prevention of CMV infection by immunization with live attenuated virus vaccine does not appear to be promising for several reasons: (1) Not only may CMV be an oncogenic virus but the live attenuated vaccine virus strains also may be oncogenic; (2) duration of immunity and degree of protection against the wild-type virus are unknown; (3) the vaccine virus might travel across the placenta and cause congenital infection; and (4) since natural immunity in the mother does not protect her offspring from congenital infection, the vaccine also seems unlikely to provide protection. Despite these problems, limited clinical studies are underway to evaluate the efficacy of a live attenuated CMV vaccine.

HERPES SIMPLEX VIRUS

Herpes simplex virus (HSV), which occasionally produces congenital infection, causes devastating disease in neonates with severe neurologic morbidity and high mortality. Cold sores (herpes labialis) and genital ulcers (herpes genitalis) are the two adult illnesses responsible for causing HSV infection in neonates. Natal HSV infection usually results from the infant's passage through an infected birth canal (maternal genital herpes); however, other factors may contribute (Table 8.9). Postnatal HSV infection is most commonly caused by transmission of the virus from an adult, frequently the mother, who has herpes labialis; but other family members and hospital personnel may be responsible. Both HSV type 1 and type 2 may cause genital herpes and neonatal disease; however, type 2 strains predominate. On the other hand, HSV-1 is generally associated with postnatal HSV infections.

Neonatal herpes infection is apparent in some infants at birth, but more commonly it appears one to three weeks postpartum. The infection may be localized to an area of skin, an eye, the oral cavity, or the central nervous system, or it may be disseminated with multiple organ involvement (Table 8.10). A large percentage of affected babies are born prematurely, and their hospital course is complicated by respiratory distress, hypoglycemia, and bacterial sepsis. Asymptomatic HSV infection appears to be uncommon.

To significantly reduce the risk of transmitting HSV infection to the newborn, women who have active genital herpes infection should be delivered by cesarean section less than four hours after rupture of membranes. Unfortunately, only about 30% of mothers whose infants acquire neonatal HSV infection have signs or symptoms of infection at or near the time of delivery. To minimize the risk of postnatally acquired infection, infants should be isolated from adults who have active oral herpes until the labial lesions become virus negative (usually about four to five days).

Before the availability of effective antiviral chemotherapy, neonatal mortality associated with HSV infection exceeded 65%, and more than 50% of survivors sustained severe sequelae, including microcephaly, mental retardation, spasticity, hemiparesis, blindness, and deafness. The devastating nature of this infection prompted an extensive search for effective therapy. Clinical trials with gamma globulin were generally unrewarding.

Table 8.8.
Approximate incidence of central nervous system sequelae following inapparent congenital cytomegalovirus infection

Sequelae	Incidence
Mental retardation	42%
Bilateral hearing loss	11%
Motor defects Spasticity Hypotonia Quadriplegia	10%
Microcephaly	3%
Chorioretinitis	2%

Table 8.9.
Risk factors associated with natally acquired herpes simplex virus infections

Active genital infection at time of delivery

History of genital herpes

Mother's exposure to sexual partner with presumed herpes simplex virus lesions

Primary rather than recurrent genital disease

Vaginal or cesarean section delivery six or more hours after rupture of membranes in a woman with active genital herpes

Table 8.10.
Clinical spectrum of neonatal herpes simplex virus infection

Type of infection	Incidence	Signs and symptoms	
Disseminated disease	64%		
Without CNS involvement	32%	Fever Vomiting Jaundice Hepatomegaly Skin vesicles Ulcers in the oral cavity	Lethargy Anorexia Purpura Keratitis Respiratory distress
With CNS involvement	32%	Signs of disseminated disease plus: Irritability Decerebrate posturing Flaccidity or spastic paralysis	Seizures Coma
Localized CNS disease	18%	Tremors Lethargy Posturing Flaccidity or spastic paralysis	Seizures Irritability Coma
Localized disease Eye Skin Mouth	17%	Keratoconjunctivitis, chorioretinitis Vesicles Ulcerative lesions	
Asymptomatic disease	<1%		

100

Studies of idoxuridine or cytarabine involved small numbers of patients in whom the therapy appeared to reduce mortality but did not influence morbidity. Recently, vidarabine significantly reduced mortality and morbidity of neonatal HSV infection. Even with this major breakthrough, mortality remains unacceptably high. Clinical studies with acyclovir, a new drug, are under way.

VARICELLA-ZOSTER VIRUS

Varicella-zoster virus (VZV), like other herpesviruses, produces both an acute infection (chickenpox) and a latent infection, which when reactivated causes disease (herpes zoster). VZV infection is not common during pregnancy, and it was not thought to produce teratogenic effects. In recent years, however, several cases of VZV-related birth defects have been reported; the infection is severe and mortality is high. The rarity of the birth defects is probably related to (1) the low incidence of chickenpox in pregnant women and (2) the possibility that VZV does not readily cross the placental barrier. Abnormalities attributed to congenital VZV infection are summarized in Table 8.11.

When maternal chickenpox occurs near term, the fetus may become infected during the viremic phase and then develop clinical disease after birth. The course of neonatal varicella is quite variable. If maternal chickenpox occurs five or more days before delivery, the neonate will frequently have a mild varicella infection within four days after birth. If, however, the onset of maternal illness is within four days of delivery, the neonatal disease appears later and is generally devastating; hyperthermia, anorexia, a macular-vesicular rash, and multiple organ failure, involving the lungs, liver, kidneys, adrenals, and brain, may occur. The presence or absence of maternal antibodies is generally believed to be a critical determinant of the infection's severity. Infants whose mothers had chickenpox five or more days before de-

Figure 8.3. A young infant with herpes-zoster infection.

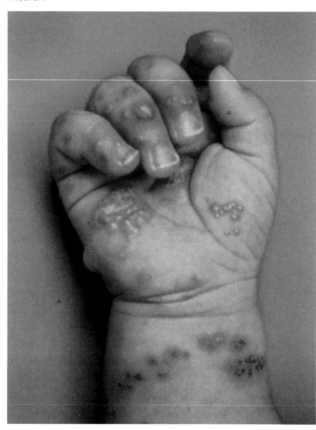

Table 8.11.
Abnormalities attributed to congenital varicella-zoster virus infection

Cutaneous scars

Hypoplasia of a limb

Low birth weight

CNS damage
Encephalitis
Cortical atrophy
Seizures
Psychomotor retardation

Paralysis with muscular atrophy of a limb

Increased susceptibility to infection

Increased infant mortality

Rudimentary digits

Chorioretinitis

Cataracts or other ocular defects or both

Clubfoot

livery have sufficient time in utero to acquire maternal antibody and, hence, some protection, whereas those whose mothers had chickenpox four or less days before delivery do not acquire antibody from the mother.

In infants (Figure 8.3), herpes zoster is identical to that in adults with the exception that infants have no antecedent chickenpox infection. However, these infants may have had chickenpox in utero and recovered with no evidence of disease at birth. VZV, then, may have remained latent only to produce herpes zoster when reactivated. Because the initial skin lesion of neonatal herpes simplex infection may simulate that of herpes zoster, a diagnosis of herpes zoster should not be made without ruling out HSV.

Congenital VZV results in severe damage and high mortality, whereas VZV in infancy is a self-limited illness without significant morbidity or mortality. The mild form of neonatal VZV is also a benign illness, whereas the severe form results in 30% mortality. Presently, treatment for most forms of perinatal VZV infection is supportive. Administration of varicella-zoster immune globulin (VZIG) to infants at risk for severe neonatal varicella may modify the disease, and the globulin should be administered. Vidarabine may be effective in treating VZV infections in immunocompromised hosts, and its use might also be considered in life-threatening perinatal VZV infections.

ENTEROVIRUSES

The enteroviruses – polio, coxsackie, and echo (enterocytopathogenic human orphan virus) – are ubiquitous viruses that may cause perinatal disease. At one time, poliovirus infection during pregnancy sometimes resulted in abortion, stillbirth, congenital malformation, or neonatal disease; but since the advent of polio vaccine, perinatal polio infections rarely occur in the United States. In contrast, perinatal infections caused by coxsackie and echoviruses are quite common. Again,

such infections may be acquired in utero, natally, or postnatally; however, congenital anomalies are rare, and most infections result from maternal illness at or around the time of delivery or from nosocomial spread of the virus within nurseries. The spectrum of disease ranges from mild illness (eg, pneumonitis, gastroenteritis, exanthematous illness, or nonspecific febrile illness) to overwhelming fatal infection with meningoencephalitis and multiple organ involvement. The clinical features of neonatal enteroviral disease (Table 8.12) resemble those of bacterial sepsis. Aseptic meningitis, gastroenteritis, or an erythematous maculopapular skin rash (Figure 8.4) may suggest the presence of an enteroviral infection, which should be considered in the newborn who is suspected of being septic but whose bacterial cultures remain sterile.

The prognosis of neonatal, nonpolio, enteroviral disease is influenced by several factors, including gestational age, age at onset of symptoms, route of viral transmission, disease severity, and virus type. Mortality may be as high as 11%, and death is more likely in infants who were premature or who have early-onset disease or severe disseminated infections (eg, myocarditis, encephalitis, or hepatitis). The increased susceptibility of low-birth-weight infants and infants infected in utero just before delivery is due both to the neonate's immature immune system and to the neonate's lack of maternal antibodies against the virus. Most infants who survive perinatal enteroviral infections do well, but neurologic sequelae follow meningoencephalitis in some.

Treatment of perinatal enteroviral infections is supportive. Perinatal polio can be prevented by the polio vaccine. Medical personnel can minimize the nosocomial spread of coxsackie and echovirus infections by isolating infants with known or suspected infections and by exercising good handwashing techniques.

102

Figure 8.4. Neonate with echovirus type 11 infection.

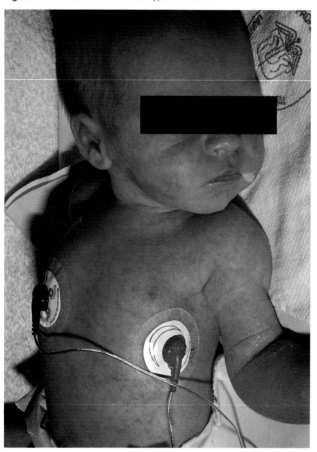

Table 8.12.
Manifestations of neonatal enteroviral infection

Signs and symptoms	Diseases
Hyperthermia	Aseptic meningitis
Hypothermia	Meningoencephalitis
Lethargy	Encephalitis
Poor eating	Hepatitis
Irritability	Gastroenteritis
Diarrhea	Adrenal cortical necrosis
Abdominal distention	Febrile exanthem
Hepatomegaly	Myocarditis
Rash	Pneumonitis
Jaundice	Pancreatitis
Seizures	Bronchitis
Emesis	
Apnea	

HEPATITIS B VIRUS

Perinatal hepatitis B virus (HBV) infections are well documented and generally transmitted from mother to infant although intrafamilial spread and transmission by blood transfusion have been reported. Mother-to-infant transmission may occur if mothers are chronic carriers of HBV or if acute hepatitis B occurs during pregnancy. The presence of hepatitis B surface antigen (HBsAg) in the maternal serum indicates the presence of HBV infection. Another antigen associated with hepatitis B, HBeAg, has recently been described, and its presence in maternal serum is associated with a high incidence of transmission of hepatitis B to offspring. Neonates born to chronic carriers may have HBsAg antigenemia at two to five months of age. This indicates exposure to HBV at birth, which may result during passage through infected vaginal secretions or exposure to maternal blood. Infants born to mothers who have acute hepatitis in the last trimester may develop an antigenemia at one to two months of age, and this suggests that an in utero infection had occurred.

The course of perinatal HBV infection varies. Most infected infants have no signs of acute infection but demonstrate either transient or persistent HBsAg antigenemia. Other infants have, in addition to the antigenemia, mildly elevated liver enzyme levels; some infants have symptomatic hepatitis, which generally resolves, but in some the infection progresses to chronic persistent or chronic active hepatitis. A few infants develop acute fulminant hepatitis.

The risk of neonatal hepatitis is quite low if the mother has acute hepatitis early in pregnancy, if she is a chronic HBsAg carrier, or if she has anti-HBe antibody. However, the risk is 50% to 75% if the mother has acute hepatitis B late in pregnancy. The long-term prognosis of asymptomatic infants with persistent HBsAg antigenemia is unknown. A few infants with perinatal HBV infection later have chronic liver disease. Although fulminant hepatitis rarely occurs, most infants who have it die. Perinatal HBV infection has not been associated with abortion, stillbirth, or congenital malformations.

The prevention of neonatal HBV infections with vaccines and hepatitis B immunoglobulin (HBIG) is being studied. Evidence suggests that administration of HBIG within 48 hours of birth and then monthly for six months can prevent hepatitis B infection in infants born to infected mothers. The results of clinical studies of antiviral drugs (interferon and vidarabine) in the treatment of adult HBV infections have been promising, but that use is still experimental; hence treatment of neonatal HBV infection is largely supportive.

RESPIRATORY SYNCYTIAL VIRUS

Respiratory syncytial virus (RSV), the major cause of bronchiolitis and pneumonia in infants less than 1 year of age, is also an important etiologic agent in neonatal disease. The clinical course is variable. Neonates may be asymptomatic; they may become mildly ill with coryza, cough, and wheezing; or they may become severely ill with severe cough, dyspnea, and radiographic evidence of pneumonia (Figure 8.5). Apnea is another striking feature; in one study, 24 of 64 (38%) neonates developed apneic episodes. The mechanism by which RSV causes apnea is unknown; but interestingly, the incidence is substantially higher in infants born prematurely and in neonates than in older infants. The association between RSV infection and apnea has led to the speculation that some cases of sudden infant death syndrome (SIDS) resulted from RSV infection. RSV is not known to cause congenital infection or natally acquired disease.

The prognosis of RSV infection is being modified as more is learned about the disease. Death is uncommon except in infants who have underlying congenital heart disease, in which mortality may exceed 35%. Whether RSV causes SIDS remains to be established; survivors of RSV appear to recover completely although long-term

Figure 8.5. Chest radiograph of a neonate with respiratory syncytial virus pneumonia.

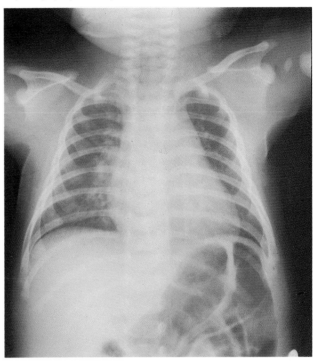

studies suggest an association between infant RSV infections and the development of chronic lung disease in later life.

Treatment is supportive. Efforts to develop a vaccine have been unrewarding. Breast-feeding may afford some protection; however, large studies are necessary to confirm this observation. Nosocomial spread is a significant cause of RSV disease within nursery populations. Procedures to prevent nosocomially acquired disease (such as careful handwashing) should be implemented.

Selected References

General
Glasgow LA, Overall JC Jr: Viral and protozoal perinatal infections of the fetus and newborn, in Behrman RE (ed): *Neonatal-Perinatal Medicine; Diseases of the Fetus and Infant*. St Louis, The CV Mosby Co, 1977, pp 270-285.

Hanshaw JB, Dudgeon JA: *Viral Diseases of the Fetus and Newborn*. Philadelphia, WB Saunders Co, 1978.

Overall JC Jr: Viral infections of the fetus and neonate, in Feigin RD, Cherry JD (eds): *Textbook of Pediatric Infectious Diseases*. Philadelphia, WB Saunders Co, 1981, pp 684-721.

Remington JS, Klein JO: *Infectious Diseases of the Fetus and Newborn Infant*. Philadelphia, WB Saunders Co, 1976.

Diagnosis of Perinatal Viral Infections
Lennette EH, Schmidt NJ: *Diagnostic Procedures for Viral, Rickettsial and Chlamydial Infections*, ed 5. Washington, DC, American Public Health Association, 1979.

Rubella
Cooper LZ: Congenital rubella in the United States, in Krugman S, Gershon AA (eds): *Infections of the Fetus and Newborn Infant*. New York, Alan R Liss, 1975, pp 1-22.

Dudgeon JA: Congenital rubella. *J Pediatr* 87:1078-1086, 1975.

Cytomegalovirus
Ballard RA, Drew WL, Hufnagle KG, et al: Acquired cytomegalovirus infection in preterm infants. *Am J Dis Child* 133:482-485, 1979.

Panjvani ZFK, Hanshaw JB: Cytomegalovirus in the perinatal period. *Am J Dis Child* 135:56-60, 1981.

Herpes Simplex Virus
Nahmias AJ, Visintine AM, Reimer CB, et al: Herpes simplex virus infection of the fetus and newborn, in Krugman S, Gershon AA (eds): *Infections of the Fetus and the Newborn Infant*. New York, Alan R Liss, 1975, pp 63-78.

Whitley RJ, Nahmias AJ, Soong S-J, et al: Vidarabine therapy of neonatal herpes simplex virus infection. *Pediatrics* 66:495-502, 1980.

Whitley RJ, Nahmias AJ, Visintine AM, et al: The natural history of herpes simplex virus infection of mother and newborn. *Pediatrics* 66:489-494, 1980.

Varicella-Zoster Virus
Gershon AA: Varicella in mother and infant: Problems old and new, in Krugman S, Gershon AA (eds): *Infections of the Fetus and the Newborn Infant*. New York, Alan R Liss, 1975, pp 79-95.

Myers TD: Congenital varicella in term infants: Risk reconsidered. *J Infect Dis* 129:215-217, 1974.

Enteroviruses
Lake AM, Lancer BA, Clark JC, et al: Enterovirus infections in neonates. *J Pediatr* 89:787-791, 1976.

Morens DM: Enteroviral disease in early infancy. *J Pediatr* 92:374-377, 1978.

Hepatitis B Virus
Dupuy JM, Giraud P, Dupuy C, et al: Hepatitis B in children. *J Pediatr* 92: 200-204, 1978.

Gerety RJ, Schweitzer IL: Viral hepatitis type B during pregnancy, the neonatal period, and infancy. *J Pediatr* 90:368-374, 1977.

Respiratory Syncytial Virus
Bruhn FC, Mokrohisky ST, McIntosh K: Apnea associated with respiratory syncytial virus infection in young infants. *J Pediatr* 90:382-386, 1977.

Hall CB: Respiratory syncytial virus, in Feigin RD, Cherry JD (eds): *Textbook of Pediatric Infectious Diseases*. Philadelphia, WB Saunders Co, 1981, pp 1247-1267.

Miscellaneous Viral Diseases

Robert B. Couch, MD

Professor, Departments of Microbiology
and Immunology, and Medicine
Director, Influenza Research Center
Baylor College of Medicine
Houston, TX 77030

HEPATITIS

Approximately 60,000 cases of acute hepatitis are reported in the United States each year, but an estimated 500,000 or more cases actually occur. Although the disease can be caused by alcohol, industrial hepatotoxins, drugs, hypoxia, leptospira, Q fever, or syphilis organisms, viruses are the most common cause (Table 9.1). Hepatitis viruses that typically do not affect organs other than the liver are A, B, and non-A, non-B. Former names for these virus infections are listed in Table 9.2.

Hepatitis A

Hepatitis A is caused by enterovirus type 72. The virus is a small (27 nm) single-stranded RNA virus without an envelope; it is lighter, has a smaller genome, and is more heat resistant than other enteroviruses. It survives temperatures up to 60°C for one hour, but it is destroyed by boiling for 20 minutes and by chlorination.

Hepatitis A occurs worldwide. According to seroepidemiologic surveys, 70% to 100% of adults in developing countries and 20% to 30% of adults in the United States show evidence of having had hepatitis A infection. At one time in the United States, the disease commonly occurred in late fall with sizeable epidemics about every seven years. Now it occurs at about the same rate throughout the year. Local epidemics are usually traceable to contaminated food or water; however, transmission by primates and other sources is also possible (Table 9.3). Although most cases of hepatitis A are subclinical (only about 10% of persons who have this antibody recall a compatible illness), rates of clinically apparent disease may be high during epidemics.

Hepatitis A is present in the feces during the preicteric and early icteric phases and is spread primarily by the fecal-oral route. It is not known whether intestinal infection occurs; however, the extensive shedding of virus in feces before any apparent liver involvement suggests that it does (Figure 9.1). Once the virus reaches the liver,

Table 9.1.
Viruses that cause acute hepatitis

Common causes	Uncommon causes
Hepatitis A	Yellow fever virus (not in the United States)
Hepatitis B	Herpes simplex virus
Non-A, non-B hepatitis	Varicella-zoster virus
Epstein-Barr virus	Rubella virus
Cytomegalovirus	Enteroviruses

Table 9.2.
Synonyms for hepatitis viruses A, B, and non-A, non-B

Current name	Former names
Hepatitis A	Infectious hepatitis Epidemic hepatitis Catarrhal jaundice
Hepatitis B	Serum hepatitis Homologous serum hepatitis Posttransfusion hepatitis Inoculation hepatitis
Non-A, non-B hepatitis	Serum hepatitis Homologous serum hepatitis Posttransfusion hepatitis Inoculation hepatitis

Table 9.3.
Transmission of viral hepatitis

Manner of transmission	Hepatitis A	Hepatitis B	Hepatitis non-A, non-B
Food, water, shellfish	+	−	−
Primate to human	+	−	−
Person to person			
Within family	+	+	+
Within an institution*	+	+	+
Venereal	−	+	?
Mother to newborn	−	+	+
Contaminated blood or blood product			
Transfusion	Rare	+	+
Syringe or needle	−	+	+
Dialysis related	−	+	+

*Persons in close and frequent contact, such as in a mental institution.

Figure 9.1. A typical course of hepatitis A infection with jaundice.

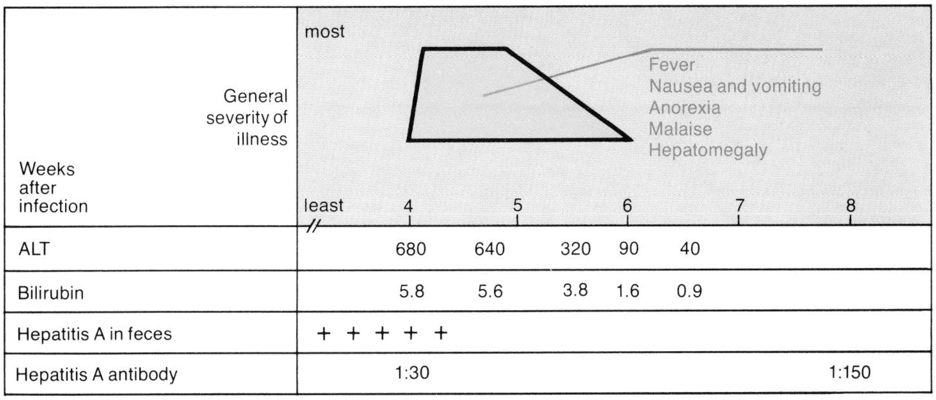

Weeks after infection	General severity of illness					
	most				Fever Nausea and vomiting Anorexia Malaise Hepatomegaly	
	least	4	5	6	7	8
ALT		680	640	320	90	40
Bilirubin		5.8	5.6	3.8	1.6	0.9
Hepatitis A in feces	+ + + + +					
Hepatitis A antibody	1:30				1:150	

presumably via the portal circulation, replication occurs and a transient low-level viremia develops. Whether liver-cell necrosis results directly from viral replication or from an immunologic reaction to the virus or virus-infected cells is not known; however, the immunologic reaction seems more plausible because of (1) the appearance of disease at the same time that an immune response is detectable and (2) the similar pathology of all hepatitis viruses. Virus disappears from the feces just before or shortly after onset of clinical disease, but it may persist in liver tissue. Serum antibody develops, and evidence indicates that complete immunity to reinfection results.

After a 15- to 50-day incubation period, the virus produces a sudden onset of disease with flu-like symptoms, including fever, headache, malaise, myalgias, nausea, and vomiting. Anorexia is prominent, and patients lose taste for food and cigarettes. A few days later, the urine becomes dark. Hepatomegaly and tenderness to palpation or fist percussion of the right upper quadrant of the abdomen may be detected. Yellow sclerae, suggestive of serum bilirubin levels ≥ 3 mg%, may also be present. Serum aspartate aminotransferase (AST, SGOT) and alanine aminotransferase (ALT, SGPT) levels are commonly in the hundreds; total bilirubin is ≥ 3 mg%, with a direct-indirect ratio of 1:1; alkaline phosphatase is usually normal or minimally elevated. At the height of

disease, a liver biopsy typically reveals liver-cell necrosis, lobular disarray, mononuclear cell infiltration, and some cholestasis. Symptoms slowly diminish. Jaundice usually lasts for one to two weeks although ALT levels may remain elevated for several weeks. After recovery, the liver is normal. Table 9.4 presents the clinical features of hepatitis A.

The clinical course of most hepatitis A infections is not predictable; many are inapparent, many are nonicteric, and many lack a clear preicteric prodrome. Fulminant hepatitis proceeds rapidly to total liver necrosis and sometimes to death. Fulminant hepatitis is characterized by a rapidly rising bilirubin level, rapidly decreasing ALT levels, a shrinking liver (acute yellow atrophy), and hepatic encephalopathy. The mortality is about 75%.

Although hepatitis A is usually diagnosed clinically, a commercially available kit that detects IgG antibody is being modified to permit detection of IgM antibody. Because serum antibody is present at the onset of disease, a specific diagnosis could be made.

Prevention of hepatitis A infection requires the avoidance of fecal contamination. Although fecal shedding of the virus is usually completed when hepatitis A becomes clinically apparent, virus may be shed after the onset of jaundice. Preexposure and postexposure prophylaxis with immune serum globulin (ISG) is about

Table 9.4.
Clinical features of viral hepatitis

	Hepatitis A	Hepatitis B	Hepatitis non-A, non-B
Incubation period (range)	30 days (15-50)	90 days (30-180)	50 days (15-150)
Onset	Sudden	Insidious	Insidious
Fever	+++	+	+
Nausea and vomiting	+++	+	+
Skin and joint symptoms	±	++	±
Anorexia	++++	++++	++++
Hepatomegaly	+++	+++	+++
Jaundice	Variable	Variable	Variable
Duration	1-3 wk	1-2 mo	1-2 mo
Mortality	<0.5%	~2%	Low
Chronic hepatitis	0	++	+++

0 Does not occur
± Rarely occurs
+ May occur
++ Frequently occurs
+++ Very frequently occurs
++++ Always occurs

Table 9.5.
Immune serum globulin as prophylaxis for hepatitis A

	Recommended dose	Duration of effectiveness
Preexposure		
Travel to endemic area	0.02 ml/kg	3 months
	0.05 ml/kg	4-6 months
Primate caretakers	0.05 ml/kg	4-6 months
Postexposure		
Household and other close contacts	<50 lb: 0.5 ml	Longer than the risk period
	50-100 lb: 1.0 ml	
	>100 lb: 2.0 ml	

80% to 90% effective. Recommended dosages are shown in Table 9.5. Once infection becomes established, treatment is supportive only.

Hepatitis B

Hepatitis B virus is hepadnavirus 1 of the new Hepadnaviridae family. The virus is a 42 nm particle with a 27 nm cubic core that contains double-stranded DNA, a DNA polymerase, and an outer coat. The virus survives a temperature of 60°C for four hours but not for ten hours. It does not survive 98°C for one minute; however, it is stable at −20°C for years.

Hepatitis B virus is synthesized only in hepatocytes; core antigen is synthesized in the nucleus, and surface antigen is synthesized in great abundance in the cytoplasm. Newly synthesized core leaves the nucleus and is coated with HBsAg in the cytoplasm. Complete and incomplete virus particles and excess HBsAg are released into the circulation. The core exhibits a unique antigenic specificity (HBcAg), as does the coat (surface antigen or HBsAg). An additional antigen, e antigen (HBeAg), is closely related to infectivity. The coat also contains several major and minor antigenic specificities that define subtypes common to epidemiologically related cases. In the United States, the most common specificity combinations are *adw, ayw, adr,* and *ayr.*

Hepatitis B infection occurs worldwide. In developing countries, 70% to 100% of adults show evidence of past infection, compared with 5% to 20% in the United States. Although transmission of hepatitis B is most commonly associated with blood transfusions and parenteral inoculations, it can be transmitted nonparenterally (Table 9.3), for example, through breaks in oral mucous membranes. Hepatitis B infection may be asymptomatic; however, persons who acquire the virus by parenteral inoculation are particularly likely to experience clinical disease (Figure 9.2).

109

Figure 9.2. A typical course of hepatitis B infection with jaundice and complete recovery.

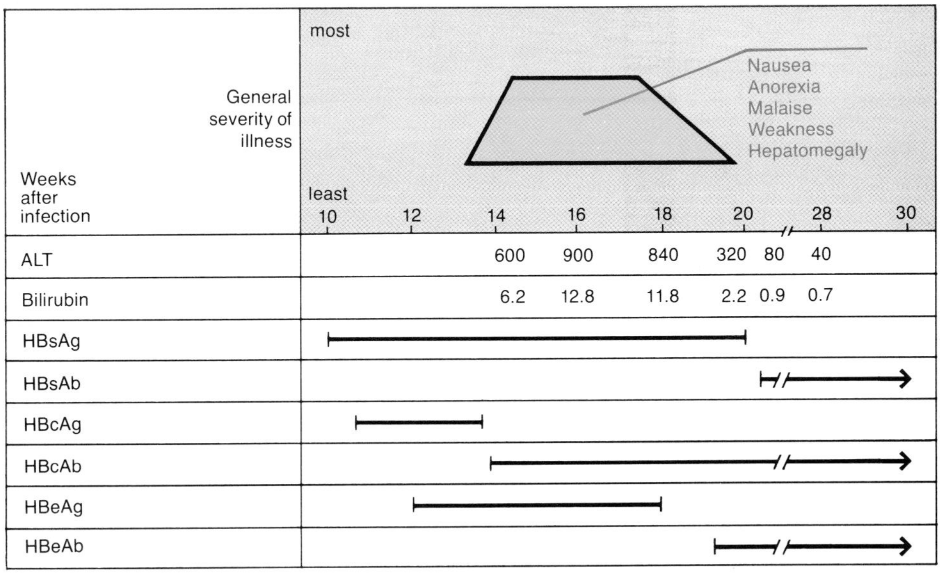

Weeks after infection	General severity of illness	10	12	14	16	18	20	28	30
ALT				600	900	840	320 80	40	
Bilirubin				6.2	12.8	11.8	2.2 0.9	0.7	
HBsAg		├──────────────────────┤							
HBsAb							├─/─────────→		
HBcAg		├──────┤							
HBcAb				├──────────────/─────────→					
HBeAg			├──────────────┤						
HBeAb							├──/─────────→		

General severity of illness: most — Nausea, Anorexia, Malaise, Weakness, Hepatomegaly — least

The incubation period for hepatitis B ranges from 20 to 180 days, but onset usually occurs about three months after exposure. Evidence suggests that the liver is primarily infected after viremia develops. HBsAg may appear three to four weeks after exposure, long before the appearance of clinical disease. HBcAg also appears and rises to a high titer, but the titer usually falls rapidly when antiHBc appears at about the onset of clinical disease. The virus does not appear to be cytopathic for cells, and this suggests that the disease is immunologically mediated. The pathology is similar to that described for hepatitis A but is frequently more severe.

Ten percent to 20% of patients develop arthritis and rash during the preicteric period, and this serum-sickness-like reaction is caused by the early appearance of antiHBs antibody and the formation of immune complexes. This syndrome may also be seen in persons who have chronic hepatitis, which indicates that antiHBs antibody exists even though it is undetectable.

As with hepatitis A, hepatitis B may range in severity from inapparent disease to fulminant hepatitis result-ing in death. Hepatitis B, however, is more likely than hepatitis A to be insidious in onset and accompanied by arthritis; fever and headache are usually absent (Table 9.4).

If HBsAg persists for more than six months, the diagnosis is *chronic hepatitis B infection* (Figure 9.3). Although a few of these patients may experience spontaneous cure, most are probably infected for life. In the United States, the incidence of chronic hepatitis is 0.1% to 0.5%; but in developing countries, it is 1% to 10%. Thus, more than 100 million people in the world have chronic hepatitis B infections.

Two disease patterns may occur — chronic persistent or chronic active hepatitis; both are HBsAg positive. Patients who have chronic persistent hepatitis are usually asymptomatic but may have mild elevation of serum ALT. Minimal hepatomegaly is common, and splenomegaly may be present. Periportal mononuclear cell infiltrates are found in the liver biopsy. This syndrome, which occurs in 8% to 10% of cases, is apparently not followed by liver fibrosis. In chronic active hepatitis,

Figure 9.3. A typical course of hepatitis B infection that became chronic. Either HBeAg or HBeAb may persist long after other signs and symptoms disappear.

Figure 9.4. A typical course of infectious mononucleosis. Note the serologic pattern.

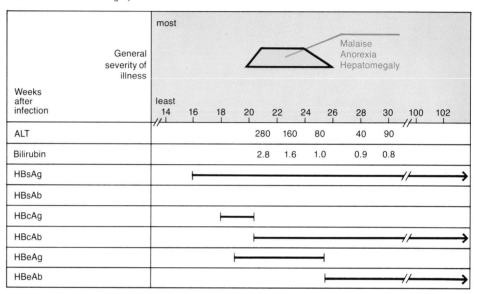

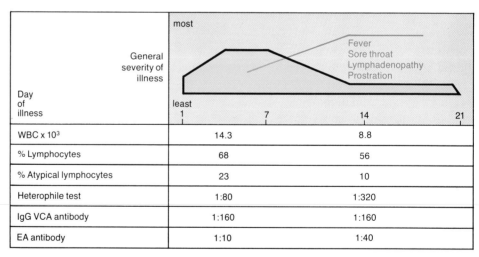

jaundice may be present, ALT levels are elevated, and the course of disease varies. Liver biopsy shows cell necrosis with lobular regeneration and fibrosis, and cirrhosis and liver failure occur in a high percentage of patients. Immune complex formation may occur during chronic hepatitis and lead to membranous glomerulo-nephritis and periarteritis nodosa.

The mechanism of recovery from hepatitis B infection is not known, but recovery is apparently accompanied by complete resistance to reinfection. Why chronic infection develops is also unknown; however, factors found to be associated with chronicity are mild infection, a long incubation period, childhood (particularly early infancy, see also chapter 8), immunosuppression, nonparenteral acquisition of infection, and genetic predisposition. About 25% of chronically infected persons exhibit liver cell necrosis, which may progress to cirrhosis and liver failure. This predisposes the infected person to liver cell cancer. Whether hepatitis B virus acts alone or as a cocarcinogen for the development of cancer is not known.

To diagnose hepatitis B infection, serum should be tested for the presence of HBsAg. The presence of anti-HBc antibody suggests recent infection, but consideration must be given to the simultaneous presence of chronic hepatitis B and other causes of acute hepatitis.

Transfusion-related hepatitis can be controlled by testing donor units of blood for the presence of HBsAg. Hyperimmune hepatitis B globulin (HBIG) is available for preventing hepatitis following needle exposure to HBsAg-positive blood although the degree of efficacy is somewhat uncertain. HBIG is also recommended for newborns of HBsAg-positive mothers. Immune serum globulin is recommended for lesser exposures, and it appears to be effective. A recently approved inactivated vaccine prepared from high titer HBsAg-positive serum provided protection to 90% to 95% of the participants in clinical trials. Therapy of hepatitis B infection is supportive. The effects of interferon and viral DNA inhibitors on chronic active hepatitis are being studied.

Non-A, non-B hepatitis
In the United States, about 90% of cases of posttransfusion hepatitis and some cases of sporadic hepatitis are caused by non-A, non-B hepatitis viruses. The number of viruses involved is unknown, but epidemiologic and experimental studies suggest that at least two exist. The incubation period ranges from 15 to 150 days (Table 9.4), and the epidemiology and disease transmission are similar to those of hepatitis B infection. Clinical disease is also similar but tends to be milder; nevertheless, severity is variable, fulminant or chronic hepatitis may develop, and cirrhosis can result.

Because pathology and laboratory findings are similar to those with hepatitis A and B, diagnosis is made by excluding A and B.

For preventing non-A, non-B hepatitis caused by needle exposure, immune serum globulin may be used if hepatitis B virus is known not to be the cause. Treatment of disease is supportive only.

GASTROENTERITIS
Acute gastroenteritis is a clinical term applied to short-term gastrointestinal disease with symptoms ranging from mild, watery diarrhea without fever to severe, febrile illness with vomiting, diarrhea, and prostration. Infants and children are affected most often. Disease may be caused by infectious agents, such as viruses, bacteria, and parasites, and noninfectious agents, such as organic toxins, metals, and drugs. Nevertheless, the cause can be identified in fewer than half the cases. In developing countries, gastroenteritis is responsible for more than half the deaths of preschool children; and in the United States it is second to the common cold in causing persons to seek medical attention.

Viruses that may produce acute gastroenteritis include rotaviruses, Norwalk viruses, enteroviruses, adenoviruses, caliciviruses, and coronaviruses. Evidence does not show that enteroviruses and adenoviruses contribute significantly, despite a very high intestinal infection rate; however, the rotaviruses and Norwalk viruses do contribute significantly.

Rotaviruses
These nonlipid-coated, double-stranded, segmented RNA viruses are 70 nm in diameter, relatively resistant to heat, and stable at $-20°C$.

The viruses appear to spread by the fecal-oral route, and more than 50% of family contacts develop infection. The viruses primarily infect the intestinal mucosa, where villous shortening, clubbing, and mononuclear cell infiltrations occur. Serum antibody is not protective, but secretory IgA antibody apparently is. In infants, most infections with serotype 2 result in clinical illness, compared with only about half the infections with serotype 1. Symptoms, which may be severe, include vomiting, diarrhea, dehydration, fever, irritability, and pharyngeal erythema. Symptoms may persist for seven to ten days, but severe disease usually lasts two to three days. It is sometimes fatal. In adults, infection is usually asymptomatic, but mild episodes of gastroenteritis may occur.

Diagnostic procedures once involved electron microscopic examination of stool samples for the presence of virus; however, this method is being replaced by another highly efficient method, ELISA (enzyme-linked immunosorbent assay). Serologic responses are best detected in complement fixation tests.

Recovery from infection is accompanied by some immunity although it is apparently incomplete. Prevention is limited to good personal hygiene and community sanitation programs. Treatment is supportive.

Norwalk viruses

The Norwalk viruses, 27 nm particles with cubic symmetry and no envelope, appear to be parvoviruses or caliciviruses. They are relatively heat resistant and quite stable.

These viruses cause gastroenteritis epidemics within families and communities. The famous outbreak in Norwalk, Ohio, was thought to have been spread by water, and many community outbreaks are attributable to contaminated water supplies. Many cases are spread by the fecal-oral route. Multiple antigenic types of Norwalk viruses appear to exist. In the United States, seroepidemiologic studies with the Norwalk virus showed that in one population tested, antibody was present in 11% of children 3 to 4 years old and in 50%

of people over 40 years old.

The viruses directly infect the intestinal mucosa. Histopathologic alterations similar to those caused by rotaviruses result, and mild clinical malabsorption occurs. Neither serum nor secretory IgA antibody is protective. After an incubation period of one to two days, the illness has a sudden onset. Both vomiting and diarrhea usually occur, but either may occur alone. Abdominal cramps are mild; and when diarrhea occurs, it usually consists of four to eight stools per day. Fever may occur, but systemic symptoms are mild. The illness lasts two to three days.

Diagnosis requires electron microscopic examination of stools for the presence of virus, but the use of reagents for serology is increasing. Prevention is limited to good community sanitation programs and personal hygiene; treatment is supportive.

INFECTIOUS MONONUCLEOSIS AND EPSTEIN-BARR VIRUS

Infectious mononucleosis (Figure 9.4) is a distinct syndrome that commonly occurs in persons between 15 and 25 years of age. Major features include generalized lymphadenopathy, peripheral blood lymphocytosis with a high proportion of atypical lymphocytes, and serum heterophile antibody (antibody for animal red blood cells). If the heterophile antibody test is negative, patients are said to have heterophile-negative mononucleosis.

Characteristics of various mononucleosis syndromes are compared in Table 9.6. Epstein-Barr virus is most commonly associated with infectious mononucleosis. Infections that occasionally produce mononucleosis-like syndromes include such diverse diseases as brucellosis, cat scratch fever, rubella, roseola, cytomegalovirus, toxoplasmosis, and viral hepatitis.

Epstein-Barr virus (EBV) is a herpesvirus, and its morphology, properties, and method of replication are similar to those of other herpesviruses. Like cytomegalovirus, it is lymphotrophic. It replicates in B-lymphocytes

Table 9.6.
Infectious mononucleosis syndromes

Infecting agent	Clinical findings in typical cases				
	Sore throat	Lymphadenopathy	Lymphocytosis	Atypical lymphocytes	Heterophile Ab
Epstein-Barr virus	+++	+++	+++	+++	+++
Cytomegalovirus	0	+	+++	+++	0
Viral hepatitis	0	+	++	++	0
Toxoplasmosis	+	+++	++	++	0

0 Usually absent   + Mild   ++ Moderate   +++ Severe

but not in T- or null-lymphocytes. Infection of lymphocytes is detectable by their transformation to a lymphoblastoid state.

The infection occurs worldwide, but the disease is limited essentially to adolescents and young adults in higher socioeconomic groups. In developing countries and lower socioeconomic groups, the infection is likely to occur during early childhood. Infections at this age are mostly asymptomatic, but nonspecific febrile illnesses may be seen. The infection is poorly communicable, shows no seasonal predilection, and does not become epidemic. Virus is present in the throat during acute illness and for up to 18 months after recovery. Close and intimate contact is required for most transmissions; however, transmission by blood transfusion is possible. In the United States, 10% of college students become infected, and of these, 10% to 60% become ill.

Initially, the virus infects oral mucosa and submucosal lymphocytes. Virus or virus-infected lymphocytes then circulate and infect lymphoid organs throughout the body.

The EBV incubation period is 30 to 50 days, after which disease onset is usually insidious with a prodrome of malaise, anorexia, and fever. Sore throat appears and becomes the most prominent symptom. Diffuse pharyngeal erythema, sometimes with exudates, is present. Lymphadenopathy is most prominent in the neck, and the spleen is palpable in more than 50% of patients. Hepatomegaly and a macular rash may also be present;

ampicillin therapy will precipitate the rash in 90% to 100% of patients. Most patients have more than 50% lymphocytes and more than 10% atypical lymphocytes (Figure 9.5) in peripheral blood.

EBV infection may also appear as a nonspecific febrile illness, hepatitis, meningoencephalitis, Guillian-Barré syndrome, or other neurologic disease. In some patients atypical lymphocytes may be rare or absent, and such patients may be heterophile negative.

The test for serum heterophile antibodies is most useful for diagnosing infectious mononucleosis. Titers of 1:40 and above are diagnostic if appropriate absorption patterns result (Table 9.7). The commercially available rapid slide tests for heterophile antibodies are both sensitive and specific. Although not generally needed, a specific diagnosis of EBV infection may be made with tests for EBV antigen (Table 9.8).

The usual course of infection is two to three weeks. Recovery is thought to require lymphocytes and macrophages; immunity to reinfection is complete and associated with viral capsid antibody. Generally, treatment is supportive; however, hemolytic anemia, severe thrombocytopenia, and airway obstruction are treated with corticosteroids.

Complications of the infection are uncommon but include hemolytic anemia, thrombocytopenia, jaundice, splenic rupture, a variety of neurologic diseases, and myocardial disease. Of particular interest are Burkitt's lymphoma and nasopharyngeal (NP) carcinoma; in cases

Table 9.7.
Absorption patterns for heterophile antibodies

Disease	Antibody removed by absorption with...	
	Guinea pig kidney cells	Beef red cells
Infectious mononucleosis	No	Yes
Serum sickness	Yes	Yes
Normal serum (Forssman antibody)	Yes	No

Table 9.8.
Serologic test for specific Epstein-Barr virus antigens

Antigen	Serologic test	Antigen titer usually rises...	Percentage of patients with increased titer
Viral capsid			
IgG VCA	IF*	Before illness onset	100
IgM VCA†	IF	Before illness onset	100
Early†	IF	Early after illness onset	70-80
Nuclear	IF	Late after illness onset	100
Membrane	IF	Late after illness onset	100
Soluble	CF‡	Late after illness onset	100

*Immunofluorescence
†Most useful for diagnosis
‡Complement fixation

Table 9.9.
Major causes of parotid gland enlargement

Unilateral enlargement	Bilateral enlargement
Mumps virus infection	Mumps virus infection
Staphylococcal infection	Certain drugs
Tumor	
Ductal obstruction (stone, stricture)	

of African Burkitt's lymphoma and in all cases of African and Oriental NP carcinoma, persistent EBV infection is present in the tumors. Although the association is strong, the absence of persistent EBV in patients with American lymphoma and some NP carcinomas suggests that the role of EBV may be that of a cocarcinogen.

PAROTITIS AND MUMPS VIRUS

Mumps virus, a paramyxovirus closely related to the parainfluenza viruses, is one major cause of parotid gland swelling (Table 9.9) although the incidence of infection has decreased significantly since the mumps vaccine became available. Virus initially grows in the upper respiratory tract and lymph nodes, then enters the bloodstream, and seeds the parotid glands. At the time of primary viremia or during secondary viremia from the parotid gland, other organs may become infected. Most commonly, meningitis and orchitis in postpubertal males may develop, but the ovaries, pancreas, and cerebral cortex (encephalitis) may also be affected. Orchitis is usually unilateral and rarely results in sterility. Involvement of the pancreas is postulated to lead to juvenile diabetes mellitus, but proof is lacking.

The incubation period is two to four weeks, and a mild, systemic prodrome precedes parotid swelling. Swelling increases for two to three days, and local pain may be prominent. Bilateral disease occurs in 10% of cases, as does submandibular involvement. After about three days, fever and pain abate, and swelling rapidly regresses. Local complications are rare, but a variety of neurologic complications has been reported.

Mumps is usually diagnosed clinically, but the diagnosis may be confirmed by complement fixation or hemagglutination inhibition tests. Definitive proof that mumps virus rather than a parainfluenza virus is the cause requires virus isolation; because viruria occurs in 70% of acute cases, urine is a good specimen.

Therapy is supportive only. Mumps infection is noted

for being poorly communicable. It can be prevented with a highly effective live virus vaccine, which is administered subcutaneously as a single dose to youngsters who are about 15 months old. Its effect may last a lifetime.

KERATITIS AND CONJUNCTIVITIS

The conjunctivae and the cornea may become infected with bacteria, fungi, parasites, chlamydiae, or viruses. Adenovirus or herpes simplex type 1 are the viruses most likely to be responsible. Pharyngoconjunctival fever caused by adenoviruses is described in chapter 6.

Epidemic keratoconjunctivitis (EKC), which is caused by type 8 and sometimes types 19 and 37 adenovirus, is chiefly an occupational disease among persons who have frequent eye injuries (shipyard workers), or it may result from contaminated ophthalmic instruments. The incubation period is three to 14 days, after which pain, photophobia, lacrimation, and blepharospasm occur. Preauricular adenopathy is also prominent. After a few days, punctate opacities appear on the cornea and may remain for weeks (Figure 9.6). Clinical findings are distinctive. Viral isolation requires conjunctival and corneal scrapings.

Characteristics of herpes simplex conjunctivitis are similar to those described for adenovirus conjunctivitis. Most infections do not affect the cornea. However, when they do, the lesions can have a variety of shapes. Characteristic herpetic lesions appear as dendrites (Figure 9.7). Conjunctival and corneal specimens may be used for viral isolation. (See also chapter 5.)

Treatment of adenovirus EKC is supportive, but herpes simplex corneal disease may be treated with agents such as idoxuridine, vidarabine, or trifluorothymidine.

MYOCARDITIS AND PERICARDITIS

Acute myocarditis and acute benign pericarditis are common diseases, but proof of a viral etiology is uncommon.

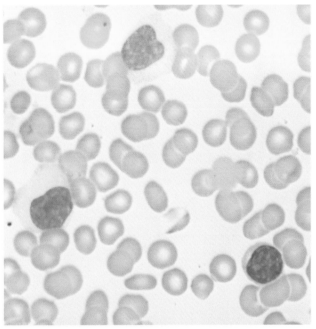

Figure 9.5. Atypical lymphocytes in the peripheral blood of a patient who has infectious mononucleosis. The large cells with lobulated nuclei and pale blue cytoplasm containing vacuoles are atypical lymphocytes.

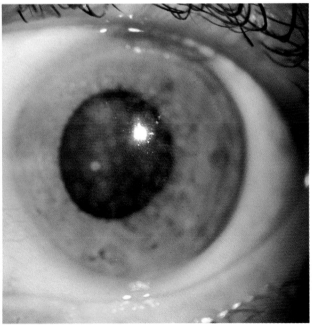

Figure 9.6. Keratoconjunctivitis caused by adenovirus. The punctate subepithelial opacities have persisted in this patient.

116

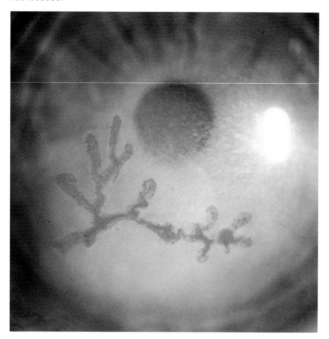

Figure 9.7. Keratitis caused by herpes simplex virus. Note the dendritic opacity. Conjunctivitis has receded.

Most definitive information concerning viral myocarditis and pericarditis has come from reports of epidemics of enteroviral infections in which heart involvement clearly occurred. Coxsackie B viruses have been responsible most often.

The patients are acutely ill and have fever and systemic symptoms; involvement of the heart is indicated by chest pain or shortness of breath. Abnormal findings are usually detected during cardiovascular examination, but electrocardiograms are always abnormal. Residual cardiac abnormalities after clinical recovery are common.

TUMORS

Viruses cause tumors in humans and in animals. Benign tumors include the smooth-surfaced, scattered lesions of the poxvirus *Molluscum contagiosum* and the papillomatous lesion of the orf virus. The most common tumors are warts, which are caused by a papillomavirus. The virus, acquired by direct cutaneous inoculation, stimulates cell division. Warts are classified by shape and location as the common wart, flat wart, plantar wart (soles or palms), or condyloma acuminatum (genital or anal papillomas).

Possible virus-related malignant tumors in humans include carcinoma of the cervix (herpes simplex virus), carcinoma of the liver (hepatitis B virus), and Burkitt's lymphoma and nasopharyngeal carcinoma (Epstein-Barr virus). Recently in the United States, strong evidence that a retrovirus causes many T-cell leukemia lymphomas has been provided. Two or three types of this human T-cell leukemia lymphoma virus (HTLV) exist, and infection is prevalent among persons in southern Japan and the Caribbean region.

Selected
References

Baum SG, Litman N: Mumps virus, in Mandell GL, Douglas RG, Bennett JE (eds): *Principles and Practice of Infectious Diseases.* New York, John Wiley & Sons, 1979, pp 1176-1185.

Blacklow NR, Cukor G: Medical progress: Viral gastroenteritis. *N Engl J Med* 304:397-406, 1981.

Blattner WA, Blayney DW, Robert-Guroff M, et al: Epidemiology of human T-cell leukemia/lymphoma virus. *J Infect Dis* 147:406-416, 1983.

Dienstag JL: Non-A, non-B hepatitis. *Adv Intern Med.* 26:187-233, 1980.

Dolin R: Norwalk-like agents of gastroenteritis, in Mandell GL, Douglas RG, Bennett JE (eds): *Principles and Practice of Infectious Diseases.* New York, John Wiley & Sons, 1979, pp 1364-1370.

Duff DF: Myocarditis: Viral and bacterial myocarditis, in Feigin RD, Cherry JD (eds): *Textbook of Pediatric Infectious Diseases.* Philadelphia, WB Saunders Co, 1981, pp 255-269.

Evans AS, Neiderman JC: Epstein-Barr virus, in Evans AS (ed): *Viral Infections of Humans: Epidemiology and Control.* New York, Plenum Publishing Corp, 1976, pp 209-233.

Feldman HA: Mumps, in Evans AS (ed): *Viral Infections of Humans: Epidemiology and Control.* New York, Plenum Publishing Corp, 1976, pp 317-332.

Greer KE: Papillomavirus (warts), in Mandell GL, Douglas RG, Bennett JE (eds): *Principles and Practice of Infectious Diseases.* New York, John Wiley & Sons, 1979, pp 1362-1364.

Hollinger FB, Dienstag JL: Hepatitis viruses, in Lennette EH (ed): *Manual of Clinical Microbiology,* ed 3. Washington, DC, American Society for Microbiology, 1980, pp 899-921.

Landau JW: Warts (papovaviruses): Molluscum contagiosum, in Feigin RD, Cherry JD (eds): *Textbook of Pediatric Infectious Diseases.* Philadelphia, WB Saunders Co, 1981, pp 643-648.

Lerner AM: Myocarditis and pericarditis, in Mandell GL, Douglas RG, Bennett JE (eds): *Principles and Practice of Infectious Diseases.* New York, John Wiley & Sons, 1979, pp 711-724.

McCollum RW: Viral hepatitis, in Evans AS (ed): *Viral Infections of Humans: Epidemiology and Control.* New York, Plenum Publishing Corp, 1976, pp 235-249.

Purcell RH: The viral hepatitides. *Hosp Pract* July:51-63, 1978.

Rapp CE Jr, Hewetson JF: Infectious mononucleosis and the Epstein-Barr virus. *Am J Dis Child* 132:78-86, 1978.

Reitz MS Jr, Kalyanaraman VS, Robert-Guroff M, et al: Human T-cell leukemia/lymphoma virus: The retrovirus of adult T-cell leukemia/lymphoma. *J Infect Dis* 147:399-405, 1983.

Robinson WS: Hepatitis A virus, in Mandell GL, Douglas RG, Bennett JE (eds): *Principles and Practice of Infectious Diseases.* New York, John Wiley & Sons, 1979, pp 1370-1388.

Robinson WS: Hepatitis B virus, in Mandell GL, Douglas RG, Bennett JE (eds): *Principles and Practice of Infectious Diseases.* New York, John Wiley & Sons, 1979, pp 1388-1424.

Robinson WS: Non-A, non-B hepatitis, in Mandell GL, Douglas RG, Bennett JE (eds): *Principles and Practice of Infectious Diseases.* New York, John Wiley & Sons, 1979, pp 1424-1430.

Schackelford PG, Smith M: Ocular infections, in Feigin RD, Cherry JD (eds): *Textbook of Pediatric Infectious Diseases.* Philadelphia, WB Saunders Co, 1981, pp 661-683.

Schleupner CJ, Overall JC Jr: Infectious mononucleosis and Epstein-Barr virus. *Postgrad Med* 65:83-105, 1979.

Schooley RT, Dolin R: Epstein-Barr virus (infectious mononucleosis), in Mandell GL, Douglas RG, Bennett JE (eds): *Principles and Practice of Infectious Diseases.* New York, John Wiley & Sons, 1979, pp 1324-1341.

Thomas JV, Green WR: Conjunctivitis, in Mandell GL, Douglas RG, Bennett JE (eds): *Principles and Practice of Infectious Diseases.* New York, John Wiley & Sons, 1979, pp 1009-1014.

Thomas JV, Green WR: Keratitis, in Mandell GL, Douglas RG, Bennett JE (eds): *Principles and Practice of Infectious Diseases.* New York, John Wiley & Sons, 1979, pp 1015-1023.

Wyatt RG, Kapikian AZ: Viral gastrointestinal infections, in Feigin RD, Cherry JD (eds): *Textbook of Pediatric Infectious Diseases.* Philadelphia, WB Saunders Co, 1981, pp 489-507.

Yolken RH, Kapikian AZ: Rotavirus, in Mandell GL, Douglas RG, Bennett JE (eds): *Principles and Practice of Infectious Diseases.* New York, John Wiley & Sons, 1979, pp 1268-1281.

Prevention and Therapy of Viral Infections

Lawrence Corey, MD

Associate Professor of
Laboratory Medicine and Microbiology
University of Washington School of Medicine
and
Head, Virology Division
Children's Orthopedic Hospital and Medical Center
Seattle, WA 98105

Until recently, efforts to control viral infections have concentrated on immunoprophylaxis, which involves either vaccines (active immunization) or antisera (passive immunization). An increasing understanding of the molecular biology of viral replication is resulting in the development of effective chemotherapy. With these medical advances will come an increasing need for methods of rapid and specific diagnosis of viral infections.

Immunization and chemoprophylaxis are the most reliable means of preventing viral disease. The purpose of immunization is to produce a specific immune response to a virus or its antigens. This acquired immunity may be cell mediated or humoral or both. Although the protection provided by immunization may diminish over time, reexposure to the same stimulus results in an anamnestic immune response.

Many groups of viruses have characteristics that impede the development of specific vaccines. For example, the rhinoviruses have several hundred antigenically unique strains; therefore, production of a single vaccine is not feasible. The influenza viruses can undergo antigenic strain variations, which necessitate variations in the viral antigen used in vaccine preparations. The portal of entry of a virus and the role of local immunity may also be important in determining whether a parenterally administered vaccine will prevent or ameliorate disease.

Some viral infections can be prevented or ameliorated by active or passive immunization or both. Regardless of which form is used, the desired effect is protection against the pathogenic organism.

VACCINES

Compared with live attenuated virus vaccines, inactivated virus vaccines usually require more antigen to produce a similar active immune response. Inactivated virus vaccines are also associated with a less pronounced local immunity and a greater time lapse between administration of the antigen and the appearance of protective effects. Live virus vaccines have some theoretical advantages in that local and durable humoral immunity appears to be more marked than immunity produced by inactivated virus. However, viral replication following administration of live vaccine can be accentuated in patients who have immune deficiencies. For this reason, live virus vaccines should not be given to immunocompromised patients. Table 10.1 lists the viral vaccines commonly used in the United States.

Poliomyelitis

Two types of polio vaccines are licensed in the United States, oral polio vaccine (OPV) and inactivated polio vaccine (IPV). The preferred form is OPV, which is a live attenuated virus vaccine that combines all three strains of poliovirus and produces long-lasting immunity to all poliovirus types in more than 95% of recipients. Immunity is achieved in seven to ten days, and most recipients are protected after receiving a single dose. Administration of OPV may also interfere with simultaneous infection by wild polio viruses, a property of special value in campaigns to control epidemics.

OPV has rarely been associated with paralytic disease in vaccine recipients or their close contacts. In the ten years from 1969 through 1978, approximately 242 million doses of OPV were distributed in the United States, and 76 cases of paralysis associated with the vaccine were reported. This is approximately one case per three million doses. Of the 76 cases, 18 occurred in healthy vaccine recipients, 47 in healthy close contacts of vaccine recipients, and 11 in recipients or contacts who had immune deficiencies.

Table 10.1.
Virus vaccines

Immunization	Type of vaccine	Method of administration* and frequency	Comments
Poliomyelitis	Live attenuated (Sabin)	Oral polio vaccine (OPV) 3-dose primary series	Preferred for routine use and epidemics
	Formalin-inactivated (Salk)	Inactivated polio vaccine (IPV), SC in 4-dose primary series	Selective use in unimmunized adults and children in whom live virus vaccine is contraindicated
Measles	Live attenuated	SC once	Routine use and control of outbreaks, usually among adolescents or young adults
Mumps	Live attenuated	SC once	Routine use and prevention of orchitis in susceptible seronegative males
Rubella	Live attenuated	SC once	Use in females who are antibody (HI) negative and in whom pregnancy can be prevented for 3 months postvaccination and routine use in children
			Routine use and control of outbreaks among adolescents and young adults
Influenza	Inactivated	SC yearly	Directed at reducing morbidity and mortality in those at risk of influenza complications and those over age 65
Adenovirus	Live attenuated bivalent (types 4 and 7)	PO once	Used only for military recruits
Yellow fever	Live attenuated	SC once every 10 years	In United States, administered only at yellow-fever centers to persons traveling to areas where the disease is endemic
Smallpox	Live vaccinia	ID every 3-5 years	Now recommended only for military personnel
Hepatitis B	Inactivated	IM 3 doses	Recommended especially for persons with increased risk of hepatitis
Hepatitis A	Immune serum globulin	IM every 3 months	See passive immunization in this chapter
Rabies	Inactivated	SC or IM	For persons at high risk before exposure. Given with human rabies immune globulin after exposure.

*PO = orally, SC = subcutaneously, IM = intramuscularly, ID = intradermally

IPV also has been used extensively throughout the world. It is injected subcutaneously, and a series of four doses produces immunity to all three poliovirus types in more than 95% of recipients.

All infants beginning at about two months of age and preschool-aged children should receive one of the primary series of polio vaccine, which can be integrated with other immunization procedures. Supplementary immunization for children when they begin school and for adolescents is also recommended.

Because OPV is often excreted in the feces for weeks after vaccination, unvaccinated parents should also be immunized. Many health care personnel elect to give parents one or two doses of IPV one month apart before the child receives OPV. Subsequent vaccination of the child, however, must be assured. Because of the substantially increased risk of disease associated with OPV, patients who have immune deficiency diseases should be given IPV.

Measles

Measles is often a severe disease, complicated by middle ear infection, bronchopneumonia, or encephalitis. Measles illness during pregnancy is associated with premature labor and moderately increased rates of spontaneous abortion and low birth weight. Live measles vaccine is prepared in chick embryo cell cultures. The vaccine is available in monovalent form and in combination forms as measles-rubella (MR) and measles-mumps-rubella (MMR). All vaccines containing measles virus are recommended for infants who are about 15 months old. Measles antibodies develop in at least 95% of susceptible children who are vaccinated at that age or older, and the protection conferred appears to be durable. Protection is less durable in those vaccinated before age 15 months. Children vaccinated before age 12 months and people whose measles immunity cannot be confirmed should be considered susceptible to measles, and they should be revaccinated with live measles vaccine. Neither revaccination nor vaccination of people who have had measles appears to increase the risk of complications from measles vaccine. Exposure to measles is not a contraindication to vaccination. In fact, evidence suggests that administration of live measles vaccine within 72 hours after exposure may protect against disease.

Administration of immune serum globulin, 0.25 ml/kg of body weight, within six days after exposure may prevent or modify measles. This is indicated for susceptible persons, particularly infants less than 12 months old, in households with measles patients. Infants who receive this therapy should also receive live measles vaccine at age 15 months. Five percent to 15% of people vaccinated become feverish about six to 11 days after vaccination, and some have transient rashes or rare central nervous system reactions.

Mumps
Mumps is a self-limited disease that primarily involves young, school-aged children. Aseptic meningitis occurs in 15% of patients. Orchitis occurs in 20% of postpubertal males. Live mumps virus vaccine is prepared in chick embryo cell cultures and is available in monovalent form as well as in MMR form. The vaccine produces measurable antibody, which is protective and long lasting in more than 90% of susceptible persons.

Rubella
The most important objective of rubella immunization is to prevent the fetal anomalies associated with congenital rubella syndrome. The syndrome is a particular problem in children born to women who contract rubella during the first trimester of pregnancy.

Immunity appears to be long lasting after infection or vaccination with live attenuated rubella virus. Although antibody levels may decline after ten or more years, there is no evidence that routine revaccination is needed. Reexposure to natural rubella virus occasionally results in reinfection, which is highly unlikely to produce rubella embryopathy. Currently in the United States, most cases of rubella occur in adolescents and young adults, and 10% to 30% of these persons are susceptible.

In the United States, live rubella virus vaccine is prepared in either duck embryo cell culture or human diploid cell culture. The vaccine is available in a monovalent form as well as in MR or MMR forms. Vaccination produces antibodies in approximately 95% of susceptible children aged 12 months or older.

Because immunity is particularly necessary in women of childbearing age, prepubertal girls should be immunized. Vaccine should not be administered to pregnant women or to women who may become pregnant within three months after being vaccinated. However, the risk of significant rubella-vaccine-associated embryopathy is less than 3% during this period, compared with a risk of nearly 50% in women who contract wild type rubella virus during the first month of pregnancy.

Side effects most commonly associated with rubella vaccination in children are rash and lymphadenopathy. Joint pain, especially in the small peripheral joints, has been noted in up to 30% of persons vaccinated although it occurs most frequently in adult women. Frank arthritis is reported in about 1% of persons vaccinated. Joint symptoms usually begin two to ten weeks after immunization and persist for one to two weeks.

Vaccine virus has been found in the pharynx, buffy coat, and breast milk for seven to 28 days after vaccination; some evidence suggests that immunity is transmitted via breast milk to the infant; however, there is no evidence of pharyngeal transmission of attenuated virus.

Influenza

Annual influenza vaccination is strongly recommended for all people at increased risk of having complications from a lower respiratory tract infection. These people have congenital or acquired heart disease, chronic pulmonary disease, renal disease, diabetes mellitus, sickle cell disease, or immune deficiencies. Vaccination is also recommended for older persons, particularly those over age 65.

The two types of influenza vaccines are (1) inactivated whole virus vaccines, which are preferred for adults, and (2) split virus vaccines (containing either viral hemagglutinin or disrupted virion particles), which are preferred for children. Adverse reactions occur infrequently and more often in children than in adults. One such effect, Guillain-Barré syndrome (GBS), is characterized by ascending paralysis that is usually self-limited and reversible. Swine influenza vaccine has been associated with an increase in the incidence of GBS (ten cases of GBS per one million persons vaccinated); however, this increased risk has not occurred with subsequent influenza vaccines.

Adenovirus

Different adenovirus serotypes cause different diseases, such as respiratory or enteric illnesses, keratoconjunctivitis, or pharyngoconjunctival fever. Live adenovirus vaccine (types 4 and 7) is useful in controlling outbreaks of acute respiratory disease among military recruits; however, it is not available for civilians. Vaccines for other serotypes have not been developed.

Yellow fever

Yellow fever is endemic to parts of Africa and South and Central America, and vaccination is recommended for everyone over 6 months of age who travels to or lives in these areas. Yellow fever vaccine is a live attenuated virus preparation made from the 17-D strain, which is grown in chick embryo cells. A single subcutaneous injection produces durable immunity for more than ten years. Reactions to the vaccine are generally mild and include myalgias and low-grade fever in 5% to 10% of persons vaccinated.

Smallpox

The World Health Organization has classified smallpox as a disease eradicated throughout the world. Smallpox vaccine is highly effective and provides relative immunity within eight days. A high level of protection lasts for at least three years, and revaccination every three years is necessary if adequate immunity is to be maintained. Immunization against smallpox is no longer recommended in the United States; but in some countries, health authorities may still require proof of vaccination within three years preceding the time of entry. They may accept a letter written by a physician and discussing the contraindications to vaccination.

Hepatitis B

Hepatitis B vaccine is made from purified hepatitis B surface antigen. This antigen is obtained from patients infected with the virus; the antigen is purified by centrifugation and inactivated with pepsin, urea, and formalin. Results of clinical studies indicate that a regimen of three doses of the vaccine (the initial dose, the second dose one month later, and the third dose six months after the initial dose) produces an antibody response in 98% of vaccinees and protects about 95%. Vaccination is recommended for those at high risk for hepatitis B. This includes sexual contacts of persons who have acute hepatitis B, homosexual men, health care personnel at risk of exposure to acute hepatitis B, and children who live where hepatitis B is endemic. Passive immunization using hyperimmune globulin with vaccination is currently being studied and may be especially useful in protecting neonates whose mothers have hepatitis B.

PASSIVE IMMUNIZATION

If given during the disease incubation period, passive immunization can ameliorate or prevent illness. Once disease onset has occurred, however, passive immunization generally is not effective. Both hyperimmune and regular immune serum globulin containing various viral antibodies have been developed.

Immune serum globulins

Immune serum globulins (ISG) are sterile solutions containing antibody from the blood of humans. They contain 16.5% protein obtained by cold ethanol fractionation of large pools of blood plasma, and they are generally administered intramuscularly. Recently intravenous ISG preparations have been licensed for routine administration to persons with deficient humoral immune systems, such as persons with agammaglobulinemia.

Hepatitis A

The results of numerous studies show that if ISG is administered within one to two weeks after exposure to hepatitis A, illness is prevented in 80% to 90% of people. Generally, the dose is 0.02 ml/kg of body weight. If ISG is given as preexposure prophylaxis to people traveling to areas where hepatitis A is endemic, it should be administered in a dose of 0.05 ml/kg of body weight, which

should confer protection for three months.

Hepatitis B

The use of ISG for passive prophylaxis of hepatitis B is controversial; however, the results of many studies suggest that ISG prevents acute hepatitis B in 40% to 70% of patients exposed. Some studies indicate that hepatitis B immune globulin (HBIG), which is a hyperimmune globulin that contains more than 100 times as much antibody to HBsAg as ISG contains, is more effective than ISG. The use of immune globulin should not replace other forms of control that can reduce the prevalence of hepatitis B. Post exposure prophylaxis for hepatitis B should include either (1) HBIG in an initial dose of 0.05 to 0.07 ml/kg of body weight and a second identical dose 25 to 30 days later or (2) ISG in the same dosage schedule if HBIG is not available. Infants born to mothers who had acute hepatitis B in the third trimester of pregnancy or HBsAg seropositivity at delivery should be given HBIG within 24 hours after birth. In such infants, HBIG has been administered as a single dose of 0.13 ml/kg of body weight with doses repeated at three and six months of age.

ANTIVIRAL CHEMOTHERAPY

Until recently, the subject of antiviral chemotherapy has been discussed in symposia aimed at future developments in medicine rather than in monographs aimed at primary care physicians. Because of recent and continuing developments in this area, however, an understanding of antiviral chemotherapy is necessary (Table 10.2). Even though drugs directed at specific viral components are being developed, progress is difficult because of (1) the close molecular relationship between viruses and the host cells in which they replicate and (2) the enormous genotypic and phenotypic heterogeneity of viruses. Most antiviral drugs currently available appear to affect viral-specific functions or viral-specific en-

Table 10.2.
Antiviral agents

Antiviral compound	Mechanism of action	Clinical effectiveness
SELECTIVE INHIBITION		
RNA viruses		
Amantadine	May inhibit uncoating of influenza A virus and block transfer of viral nucleic acid into the host cell	Prophylaxis of influenza A infection Some efficacy with early therapy of acute influenza A
DNA viruses		
Acyclovir	Substrate for HSV-specified thymidine kinase. Phosphorylated derivative inhibitor of viral DNA polymerase	Mucocutaneous HSV infection in immunocompromised hosts Primary genital herpes Localized varicella zoster infection in immunocompromised patients Short-term prophylaxis of herpes simplex virus (HSV)
BVDU (E-5-[2-bromovinyl]-2' deoxyuridine)	Substrate for HSV-specified thymidine kinase. BVDU-5' triphosphate inhibits viral DNA polymerase	Clinical investigation
Vidarabine and vidarabine monophosphate	Competitive inhibitors of viral DNA polymerase	HSV keratitis HSV encephalitis Neonatal HSV Localized varicella zoster infection in immunocompromised patients
5-iodo-2-deoxyuridine (IUdR)	Substrate for thymidine kinase. Phosphorylated derivative competes with thymidine and is incorporated into DNA.	HSV keratitis
Phosphonoacetic acid and phosphonoformate	Inhibitor of viral DNA polymerase	Not yet established but may be somewhat efficacious in mucocutaneous HSV infections
Trifluorothymidine	Inhibits thymidylate synthetase	HSV keratitis
NONSELECTIVE INHIBITION		
RNA and DNA viruses		
Interferon	Inducer of cellular enzymes which inhibit translation of viral proteins	Being investigated in immunocompromised patients with varicella or herpes zoster infections
Ribavirin	May interfere with guanosine metabolism and affect mRNA function	Being investigated in patients with arenavirus infections. Recent evidence that aerosol ribavirin may be useful in treating influenza A and B and respiratory syncytial virus infections

zymes. In general, broad-spectrum antiviral agents have not had acceptable therapeutic ratios. The recent explosion in knowledge of molecular biometabolism suggests that many further breakthroughs in antiviral chemotherapy will occur during the next two decades.

RNA viruses

Amantadine hydrochloride is used for the prophylaxis and, in selected instances, therapy of acute influenza A infection (Table 10.2). In vitro, amantadine inhibits replication of almost all influenza A viruses but has no sig-

nificant prophylactic or therapeutic effect on influenza B, parainfluenza, or respiratory syncytial virus infections. The exact mechanism of action of amantadine is not completely understood, but the drug appears to inhibit intracellular uncoating of influenza A virus.

The drug can be given orally, it is well absorbed in the gastrointestinal tract, and it has a long half-life (24 to 30 hours). When the drug is given orally, approximately 90% is excreted in the urine. The recommended daily dosage in adults is 200 mg and in children, 4 to 8 mg/kg of body weight, up to 150 mg in 24 hours.

When used prophylactically for influenza A, the drug has been 25% to 75% effective, depending on the antibody status of the patients and the severity of the influenza A outbreak. As soon as influenza A virus appears in a community, amantadine can be given prophylactically to persons who have chronic heart, lung, renal, or metabolic disease or who are otherwise at high risk of complications resulting from influenza A infection and who have not received annual influenza vaccinations. Influenza vaccine can, however, be given at the same time prophylactic therapy is initiated. If this is done, amantadine needs to be given for only about three weeks after vaccination until immune response is adequate. Results of most studies suggest that if amantadine is given within 24 hours of the onset of symptoms, the duration of viral excretion and some upper respiratory symptoms is shorter, but whether complications associated with influenza A infection are reduced remains to be demonstrated.

DNA viruses

Several medications may be used to treat symptoms of *herpes simplex virus* (HSV) infections (Table 10.2). Most are directed at viral specific enzymes, such as DNA polymerase or thymidine kinase. For example, HSV types 1 and 2 and herpesvirus varicella-zoster (VZ) have a viral-specified thymidine kinase, but cytomegalovirus and Epstein-Barr virus, which are also herpesviruses, do not. In vitro, the antiviral drug acyclovir, which directly affects thymidine kinase, is much more active against HSV types 1 and 2 and VZ than against cytomegalovirus and Epstein-Barr virus. Results of in vitro studies with BVDU (E-5-[2-bromovinyl]-2′ deoxyuridine) show that it is selectively active against VZ to a greater extent than is acyclovir. Unfortunately, results of in vitro studies of antiviral drug activity have not provided highly accurate predictability of in vivo effectiveness.

Acyclovir (ACV) is a purine analogue that appears to be a selective substrate for viral thymidine kinase. In vitro, acyclovir is selectively phosphorylated by HSV- or VZ-infected cells. Viral-specified thymidine kinase converts acyclovir to ACV monophosphate, which is then phosphorylated by cellular kinases to ACV triphosphate. ACV triphosphate is a substrate for HSV DNA polymerase and also acts as a chain terminator of viral DNA synthesis. When acyclovir 5 mg/kg of body weight is given intravenously, it produces plasma levels of 20 to 60 micromoles. At a 10 mg/kg dose, peak levels of 100 micromoles are achieved. In vitro, the concentrations of acyclovir that effect a 50% reduction in the growth of HSV type 1, HSV type 2, and VZ viruses are approximately 0.1, 0.5, and 3.5 micromoles, respectively. In a 24-hour period, approximately 70% of the drug is excreted unchanged in the urine. The plasma half-life of orally administered acyclovir is about three hours.

Acyclovir appears to be useful for treating symptoms of HSV infections. In immunocompetent patients, it shortens the duration of viral shedding and of lesions of primary genital HSV infection; and in immunocompromised patients, it hastens the healing of mucocutaneous symptoms. These results are achieved with intravenous or topical administration although intravenous administration appears to be more efficacious. In a recent study of acyclovir in immunocompetent patients who had VZ infection, healing time, duration of viral shedding, and frequency of postherpetic neuralgia were reduced.

No significant hepatic, hematopoietic, or neurologic toxicity has been noted with acyclovir; however, rapid bolus infusion may produce crystallization of the drug in the kidney. This renal lesion is reversible and appears to be avoidable if the drug is infused over a period of one hour.

Of recent concern is the emergence of acyclovir-resistant HSV mutants in vitro and in vivo. Of the two known mechanisms of resistance, one affects the thymidine kinase locus and the other, the DNA polymerase locus. The most common mechanism is seen with HSV mutants that lack viral-specified thymidine kinase (TK). To date, however, all wild-type HSV strains have had thymidine kinase. The clinical importance of acyclovir-resistant HSV is currently unknown because TK-mutants appear to be less virulent in vitro.

Vidarabine is a competitive inhibitor of the viral DNA-dependent DNA polymerase. In vitro, it is active against HSV, VZ, cytomegalovirus, and vaccinia virus.

The drug is cleared by the kidney, and approximately 60% is excreted in urine within 24 hours after administration. The plasma half-life of intravenously administered vidarabine (also called adenine arabinoside and Ara-A) is 3.5 to 5.3 hours. In serum and cells, Ara-A is quickly deaminated to ARA-HX. Xanthine oxidase inhibitors such as allopurinol may decrease the metabolism of ARA-HX, thus generating high concentrations of vidarabine in serum and causing increased toxicity. The drug should not be administered to children who are deficient in adenine deaminase. Drug levels in cerebrospinal fluid appear to be approximately half those in serum.

Results of clinical investigations show that intravenous administration of vidarabine in doses of 15 mg/kg of body weight to HSV-infected neonates reduces mortality associated with HSV encephalitis. In immunocompromised patients who have VZ infection, vidarabine appears to decrease the duration of viral shedding, the incidence of dissemination, and the frequency of postherpetic neuralgia and to speed the rate of healing. This appears to be especially pertinent in young immunocompromised patients. Also, in a small study of primary varicella infection, vidarabine appeared to have some therapeutic effect. HSV keratitis can be treated with vidarabine ophthalmic ointment.

Vidarabine administered daily in doses of 15 mg/kg of body weight is well tolerated. About 10% of recipients complain of nausea, vomiting, and diarrhea. Five percent to 8% complain of some nervousness and jitteriness. If high concentrations are given, especially to patients who have renal failure, overt encephalopathy may occur. At daily doses of 20 mg/kg or more, bone marrow megaloblastosis may occur. Insolubility also is a problem with vidarabine.

5-iodo-2-deoxyuridine (IUdR, idoxuridine), the first antiviral drug licensed for the treatment of HSV infections, is limited in use to topical application for the treatment of herpetic keratitis. IUdR is phosphorylated by cellular enzymes, and it appears to be incorporated into DNA in virus-infected cells to a greater extent than in host cells. However, in vitro toxicity in cells not infected with virus can be demonstrated. In some cell systems, some protein synthesis still occurs in the presence of inhibited DNA synthesis. Given systemically, IUdR is associated with significant bone marrow suppression, and its penetration of cerebrospinal fluid is poor. In vitro and in vivo HSV resistance to IUdR has occurred, most commonly after repeated treatment. Most IUdR-resistant organisms are susceptible to other antiviral drugs, such as vidarabine and trifluorothymidine.

Phosphonoacetic acid (PAA) and *phosphonoformate* (PFA) are selective inhibitors of HSV DNA polymerase. Both of these compounds are being studied in topical formulations for the treatment of mucocutaneous HSV infections. In animal models, both are very effective in the treatment of genital and oral-labial HSV. In recent studies in Sweden, topical application of a 3% phosphonoacetic acid cream was well tolerated.

Trifluorothymidine: Trifluorothymidine, which is a trifluoro analogue of thymidine, was recently licensed for the treatment of HSV keratitis. At present, it appears to be the treatment of choice for large ameboid herpetic ulcers of the eye. The compound affects DNA synthesis in both host and viral-infected cells by inhibiting thymidilic synthetase. This in turn causes DNA-strand breaks and some inhibition of DNA polymerase. Because of toxicity associated with systemic administration, the drug is currently used only as a 1% ophthalmic solution.

All compounds that are available for the treatment of acute HSV infection affect the productive, or lytic, phase of the virus, but they appear to have no effect on the latent phase. Patients in whom ganglionic latency is established may use antiviral drugs to treat mucocutaneous HSV infections and thereby shorten the course of disease or prevent clinical recurrence, but ganglionic latency remains unchanged.

Inhibition of DNA and RNA viruses

Interferon: Interferons are a group of low-molecular-weight (24,000 to 26,000) glycoproteins that have antiviral properties, but they are not virus specific. They inhibit a variety of RNA and DNA viruses. The properties, pharmacology, route of administration, and spectrum of activity of interferons vary; however, they appear to play an important role in limiting viral replication at the portal of entry, in reducing viremia, and in promoting recovery from established infection. The several types of interferons are differentiated by host range, source from which they are derived, pH, and heat stability.

Virus-induced interferon (type I, alpha) differs from immune interferon (type II, gamma), which is an important mediator of cellular immunity. Type I interferon can be produced from human leukocytes, fibroblast lines, and virus-infected lymphoblastoid cell lines.

Interferons indirectly inhibit viral pathogenesis. Virus-infected cells induce the production of interferons, which then enter neighboring cells and induce the production of cellular enzymes that block viral production in these cells. Thus, interferon's antiviral activity appears to be related to its ability to inhibit the transcription and translation of viral nucleic acid. The molecular basis for this inhibition is incompletely understood.

Recent advances in molecular biology suggest that the production of large quantities of relatively purified and potent interferons is feasible. At present, all inter-feron preparations are available only as investigational drugs, and the largest clinical experience has been with human leukocyte interferon. This preparation is administered systemically, usually intramuscularly. Five to eight hours after an intramuscular injection of 80×10^6 units, maximal plasma levels of approximately 100 units/ml are achieved. Its penetration of cerebrospinal fluid appears to be poor, and little is excreted in urine. Side effects associated with human leukocyte interferon include fever, nausea, vomiting, malaise, and myalgias; local toxicity such as pain and erythema may also occur. If large doses of the drug are given, some myelosuppression may occur.

So far, most clinical studies of exogenously administered interferon have been in patients who have herpesvirus or respiratory virus infections. Because interferons are important immune modulators as well as viral inhibitors, clinical effects are probably attributable to a combination of both functions. Thus, clinical efficacy may vary with the cellular immune responses of the patients studied. For example, in a group of immunocompetent patients, the administration of exogenous interferon following trigeminal nerve surgery prevented the development of oral-labial HSV. In contrast, when administered to renal transplant recipients, it did not decrease the development of HSV infections. Interferon has, however, had some effect in decreasing cytomegalovirus excretion in renal transplant patients; but in the more immunosuppressed bone marrow transplant recipients, similar doses have provided no clinical or antiviral efficacy. In patients with rhinovirus infections, exogenously administered interferon decreased the development of the infection or ameliorated the symptoms. Further advances in molecular biology and the development of potent chemical inducers of interferons likely will extend their clinical utility.

Ribavirin is a synthetic triazole nucleoside that has a wide range of antiviral activity against such diverse viruses as the myxoviruses, arenaviruses, and herpes simplex viruses. Ribavirin's exact mechanism of action is poorly understood although it appears to inhibit the early replication cycle of both RNA and DNA viruses. Some evidence suggests that DNA and RNA synthesis is inhibited because of a depletion of the guanosine triphosphate pool in both infected and noninfected cells. Results of other studies suggest that this effect is attributable to an inhibition of RNA polymerases.

In humans, the drug appears to be rapidly absorbed by cells, including red blood cells, and phosphorylated by cellular enzymes. In clinical studies, oral ribavirin 1,000 mg administered daily for five days did not affect naturally occurring influenza A infection. However, in recent experimental studies involving rhesus monkeys with arenavirus infections, specifically Lassa fever, early administration of ribavirin appeared to reduce the severity of this devastating infection. Anecdotal reports of this infection in humans also suggest that ribavirin therapy is useful.

The major toxic effect associated with ribavirin is low-grade hemolytic anemia, evidenced by a rise in indirect bilirubin and a slight drop in hematocrit. It has been reported in 5% to 10% of recipients and reverses after ribavirin therapy is stopped.

The results of recent studies suggest that aerosol ribavirin administered into the lower respiratory tract may shorten the duration of symptoms and excretion of influenza A and B and respiratory syncytial viruses. The patients who received aerosol ribavirin experienced no toxicity. Investigations of the aerosol form of the drug continue.

IMMUNOTHERAPY

Immunotherapy, which involves the use of immune modulators to enhance resistance, is another means of ameliorating or preventing viral infections. In immunosuppressed patients, viral infections, especially herpes-virus infections, occur more frequently and more severely than in immunocompetent patients.

In experimental animals, the use of immunosuppressive agents, antilymphocyte serum, or substances that deplete monocyte macrophages appears to enhance virulence of herpesvirus infections. Specific immune modulators that could improve immune response to viral infections in immunocompromised patients are needed; however, most immune modulators studied to date have little, if any, clinical utility. For example, results of clinical studies in which levamisole, an antihelminthic, was given for HSV infections are unimpressive. Transfer factor, however, has recently been shown to be effective in preventing varicella-zoster infections in immunosuppressed patients. These findings suggest that specific immune modulators directed at cellular components of the immune response to viral pathogens may be useful. Nevertheless, many complex interactions probably occur in immune responses, and these interactions may differ among pathogens.

CONCLUSION

The past four decades have brought major developments in the understanding of viral infections as well as in methods of prevention and treatment. The most recent understanding of the molecular biology of viral replication processes provides further clues to viral pathogenicity and to differences between viruses and normal host cells. As knowledge of viral activities continues to grow, the prevention and treatment of specific viral infections will become more feasible. The resultant need for specific diagnosis of viral infections will increasingly require the skills of the viral diagnostic laboratory as well as the physician.

Selected
References

Corey L: Chemotherapy of herpes simplex virus infections, in Isselbacher K, Adams RD, Braunwald E, et al (eds): *Harrison's Principles of Internal Medicine, Update III.* New York, McGraw-Hill Book Co, 1982, pp 31-52.

Katz SL, Klein JO (eds): Prospects for new viral vaccines: A symposium. *Rev Infect Dis* 2:349-492, 1980.

Klein JO (ed): *Report of the Committee on Infectious Diseases,* ed 19. Evanston, Ill, American Academy of Pediatrics, 1982.

Nightingale EO: Recommendations for a national policy on poliomyelitis vaccination. *N Engl J Med* 297:249-253, 1977.

Schiff GM: Active immunizations for adults. *Annu Rev Med* 31:441-451, 1980.

Acknowledgments

Figure 2.10. Reprinted from *Virology* 80:260-274, 1977, with the permission of PH Yuen, PhD, and Academic Press Inc, New York.

Figure 3.1. Reprinted from the *American Journal of Pathology* 28:1047-1063, 1951, with the permission of Mrs. Dalldorf and Harper & Row Publishers Inc, Philadelphia. The Division of Laboratories and Research, New York State Department of Health, Albany, NY, kindly provided the photograph.

Figure 3.2. Reprinted from the *Bulletin of the New York Academy of Medicine* 26:329-335, 1950, with the permission of Mrs. Dalldorf and Rebecca Gifford Lloyd, DVM, and the New York Academy of Medicine. The Division of Laboratories and Research, New York State Department of Health, Albany, NY, kindly provided the photograph.

Figures 3.3a, 3.3b. Reprinted from the *Journal of Infectious Diseases* 141: 394-403, 1980, with the permission of Riad Khatib, MD, and The University of Chicago Press, Chicago, copyright 1980 The University of Chicago.

Figure 3.4. Reprinted from *Diagnostic Procedures for Viral, Rickettsial, and Chlamydial Infections,* ed 5, pp 44-45, 1979, with the permission of Royale A. Hawkes, PhD, and the American Public Health Association, Washington, DC.

Figure 3.5. Reproduced with the permission of James H. Nakano, PhD, Centers for Disease Control, Atlanta.

Figure 3.6. Reprinted from the *Journal of Infectious Diseases* 122:227-231, 1970, with the permission of Raphael Dolin, MD, and The University of Chicago Press, Chicago, copyright 1980 The University of Chicago.

Figure 3.7. Reprinted from *Archives of Virology* 59:281-284, 1979, with the permission of Doctor Hiroshi Sato and PW Albrecht, MD, and Springer-Verlag, New York.

Figure 3.8. Reproduced with the permission of Fred Rapp, PhD, The Milton S. Hershey Medical Center, The Pennsylvania State University, Hershey, Pa.

Figure 3.10a. Reproduced with the permission of Keerti Shah, MD, The Johns Hopkins University, Baltimore.

Figure 3.10b. Reproduced with the permission of Gabriele M. Zu-Rhein, MD, University of Wisconsin Medical School, Madison.

Figure 3.10c. Reproduced with the permission of Barbara Von Schmidt, MD, Children's Hospital, Oakland, Calif.

Figure 3.11. Reproduced with the permission of Elisabeth Olding-Stenkvist, MD, University Hospital, Uppsala, Sweden.

Figure 3.13. Reprinted from *Diagnostic Procedures for Viral, Rickettsial, and Chlamydial Infections,* p 155, 1979, with the permission of Denis R. Benjamin, MD, and the American Public Health Association, Washington, DC.

Figure 3.14. Reproduced with the permission of Frederick Murphy, DVM, College of Veterinary Medicine and Biosciences, Colorado State University, Fort Collins.

Figures 3.15a, 3.15b, 3.15c. Reprinted from *Science* 201: cover, August 11, 1978, with the permission of Abner L. Notkins, MD, and the American Association for the Advancement of Science, Washington, DC. Copyright by the American Association for the Advancement of Science.

Figure 4.3. Reprinted from Stringfellow DA (ed): *Interferon and Interferon Inducers. Modern Pharmacology-Toxicology Series,* 1980, cover, with the permission of Marcel Dekker Inc, New York.

Figure 6.3. Reproduced with the permission of Vernon H. Knight, MD, Baylor College of Medicine, Houston.

Figure 6.4. Reprinted from the *American Review of Respiratory Diseases* 83: 15-28, 1961, with the permission of the American Thoracic Society, New York.

Figure 6.6. Adapted with permission, from the data of William P. Glezen, MD, Baylor College of Medicine, Houston.

Figure 6.7. Reproduced with the permission of Tuenchit Khamapirad, MD, Baylor College of Medicine, Houston.

Figure 6.8. Reproduced with the permission of Stephen B. Greenberg, MD, Baylor College of Medicine, Houston.

Figures 7.4, 7.7, 7.8. Reproduced with the permission of John R. Baringer, MD, University of Utah, Salt Lake City.

Figure 7.12. Reproduced with the permission of Paul F. Bray, MD, University of Utah, Salt Lake City.

Figure 7.14. Reproduced with the permission of John J. Herbst, MD, University of Utah, Salt Lake City.

Figure 8.2. Reproduced with the permission of August L. Jung, MD, University of Utah Medical Center, Salt Lake City.

Figure 8.3. Reproduced with the permission of Charles F. Grose, MD, University of Texas Health Science Center at San Antonio.

Figure 8.4. Reproduced with the permission of James C. Overall, Jr, MD, University of Utah Medical Center, Salt Lake City.

Figure 9.5. Reproduced with the permission of Clarence P. Alfey, MD, Baylor College of Medicine, Houston.

Figures 9.6, 9.7. Reproduced with the permission of Danny B. Jones, MD, Baylor College of Medicine, Houston.

Table Chapter 5. Reprinted from Cherry JD: Non-polio enteroviruses, in Feigin RD, Cherry JD (eds): *Textbook of Pediatric Infectious Disease.* Philadelphia, WB Saunders Co, 1981, with the permission of Doctor Cherry and the WB Saunders Co.

Table 6.2. Reproduced from *Data from the National Health Survey. Acute Conditions. Incidence and Associated Disability, United States, July 1977-June 1978,* publication (PHS) 79-1560. US Dept of Health, Education, and Welfare, 1979, p 3.

Tables 8.1, 8.4. Adapted from Overall JC Jr: Viral infections of the fetus and neonate, in Feigin RD, Cherry JD (eds): *Textbook of Pediatric Infectious Disease.* Philadelphia, WB Saunders Co, 1981, with the permission of Doctor Overall and the WB Saunders Co.

Table 8.3. Adapted from Glasgow LA, Overall JC Jr: Viral and protozoal perinatal infections of the fetus and newborn, in Behrman RE (ed): *Neonatal-Perinatal Medicine,* ed 2, p 273, 1977, with the permission of The CV Mosby Co, St Louis.

Index

138

Y

Z